THE NEMU'S END SERIES:

NEMU'S END

The History, Psychology & Poetry of the Apocalypse

Volume I:

SCIENCE REVEALED

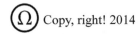

Published by Psychedelic Press
Somewhere in Albion

www.psychedelicpress.co.uk

Cover art by Ambigraph.com

PSYPRESSUK: 00005
ISBN: 978-0-9928088-0-8

for Minti,
my Nemu-sis

CONTENTS

MESSIAH APPREHENDED AT HEATHROW!

To the Manic Messianic Man

Clinical stages of type 3 [Jerusalem Syndrome]

• Anxiety, agitation, nervousness and tension, plus other unspecified reactions.

• Declaration of the desire to split away from the group or the family and to tour Jerusalem alone...

• A need to be clean and pure: obsession with taking baths and showers; compulsive fingernail and toenail cutting.

• Preparation, often with the aid of hotel bed-linen, of a long, ankle-length, togalike gown, which is always white.

• The need to scream, shout, or sing out loud psalms, verses from the Bible, religious hymns or spirituals...

• A procession or march to one of Jerusalem's holy places.

• Delivery of a 'sermon' in a holy place. The sermon is usually very confused and based on an unrealistic plea to humankind to adopt a more wholesome, moral, simple way of life.'[1]

The British Journal of Psychiatry

Jerusalem Syndrome was first described back in the 1930s, and struck with increasing frequency as the new millennium approached, with hundreds of enthusiastic tourists ranting in the streets about the end of days. The peak has become a plateau. Every year since 2000, around 40 cases have been so severe as to require hospitalisation.

Such episodes are not limited to Israel: my friend went messianic suddenly in the street in India, giving his rupees to the wind, and also giving up his daily shower. He became unmanageable at the ashram, and was eventually put in a taxi bound for the airport, where he sang *Imagine* at the check-in desk. When airport staff exchanged his stinking clothes for a cotton smock to match his scraggly beard, his *Old Testament* persona was completed. He sang Lennon's hymn again in the cabin, before throwing off his smock and launching naked into a spirited sermon. The police were waiting at Heathrow.

My own interest in things apocalyptic began in the 1990s, with a knock on the door and a fistful of colourful pamphlets depicting the fate awaiting those who would not witness Jehovah. The apocalypse, and apocalyptic people, have fascinated me ever since. From the Greek *apo-* (away) + *kalyptein* (to cover), its English synonym is *revelation,* from the Latin: 'removal' (*re*) of a 'veil' (*velum*). An apocalypse is an unveiling or disclosure, when the previously unknown becomes known, or the unconscious becomes conscious. *Nemu's End* is about the process of apocalypse. It is about how limitations arise and what happens when they collapse, both collectively in society and individually in our brains.

This book, *Science Revealed*, considers the apocalypse in science, as discovery (or **dis-cover**-y – when something hiding undercover has its *cover dissed*). Biographies of scientists such as Tesla and Einstein reveal how our most groundbreaking ideas result not from rational thinking and tapping on calculators, but from visions, dreams and other non-rational revelations. The controversies that blow up when such insights clash with embedded patterns of thought are often resolved in a manner most unscientific, and this is just one of the ways in which what is simplistically called 'rationalism' often obfuscates truth in a fundamentally complex world.

Book 2, *Neuro-Apocalypse*, is about the mechanics of revelation at the scale of the individual. We will explore how the architecture of thought channels the mind towards certain aspects of the world, and obscures others. When normal linguistic boundaries are dissolved, with autistic savantism, with degenerative brain disease, and occasionally with a knock on the head, incredible feats of perception and intuition can become possible. Meditation can also lead people to extraordinary capabilities and insights, and so can psychedelic drugs, which we will find in pre-industrial quantities in the pages of our high and holy Bible.

Book 3, *Apocalypses Past, Present and Personal*, explores the apocalypse as a collective event. At various points in history, the established structures of communities have been rapidly broken down, leaving space for new growth. This can be because of external events, such as conquest or disaster, or through the accumulation of individual insights that stress the existing order to breaking-point.

One catharsis in first century Jerusalem devastated the homeland and altered forever the self-image of the Jewish people, while launching a Jewish tale along Roman roads into the pagan world. Sublime truth or pack of lies, tool of meditation or weapon of control, something to live for, to die for, and to kill for, *The Bible* is a lean, mean, fighting meme that has self-replicated prodigiously through the centuries. It is also thoroughly embedded in the fabric of our culture, and there is much to be learned by unraveling some of its threads.

'The end of the world', for example, is a terrible translation of scripture. What ends is not the world but the aeon (or *aion* in Greek), meaning epoch or era. An apocalypse can be local, and is fundamentally individual; but upheavals can spark the same in neighbouring communities, and spread over continents. A wave of apocalypses brought the medieval age to a close, beginning with the Italian Renaissance and spreading, to the north with the Reformation, and to the west with the voyages of discovery and the birth of science. Today's international age makes for novelty on a global scale, and the pace of environmental, social and technological upheavals we face is unprecedented.

Finally, after the history, we will turn to my story, my own personal continuing apocalypse, through over a decade of ritual ayahuasca use, life-threatening illness in the Amazon, and a 6-year stint on the very mind-expanding islands of Japan.

A serpent undulates through *Nemu's End*, periodically raising his head to remove bricks from a tower of folly that has been thousands of years in the making. His case is also translated with prejudice in scripture, but the adversary (*Satan* in Hebrew) is God's left-hand man. Lucifer illuminates, as his Latin name suggests: *lucem ferre*, to bring light. Duality is a veil of illusion, and this much-maligned dark angel of light tears it down, though his lessons may be excruciating.

Another vilified agent of illumination featuring in this book is the psychedelic. While I avoid processed food and doctor's pills, and preferred the ADHD that nature gave me to the Ritalin teachers offered me, I do enjoy psychedelics, both recreational and inspirational. Used respectfully with experienced guides, as any power tool should be, they can reveal hidden things. Psilocybin, for example, makes subjects more perceptive of changes in the visual field.[2] It also induced 'full mystical experiences' in 60% of subjects in one famous experiment, leaving them measurably happier and more compassionate than controls when tested 25 years later.[3] Insights catalysed by psychedelics have given us the protocols of virtual reality, opened up whole new fields of science, sparked artistic and therapeutic modalities, and reoriented countless lives for the better. As we shall see, poets such as William Shakespeare,[4] inventors and evolutionary theorists, founders of the United States and British monarchs have all enjoyed drugs that would land them in a cell today.

Though I have had the pleasure of being given psilocybin while strapped into an magnetoencephalography machine in the name of science, my favourite tipple is ayahuasca, and my relationship with it is more rustic. This visionary tea cured my potentially fatal leishmaniasis infection during an 8-month ordeal in the Amazon, and radically changed my perspective in the process. It helped two of my friends defy terminal cancer sentences, cleared up recurrent migraines in two others, and has inspired invention, academic research and art; but it does more. Ayahuasca reveals the essence behind the mundane, a harmony that is staggering, and a world far more responsive than one might imagine. Ayahuasca, the rope (*waskha*) of the spirits (*aya*), winds its way between the worlds, and does what it says on the label. In the alchemy of plant teachers, this wonderful brew is a key to a very personal apocalypse.

Welcome to my Nemusalem Syndrome. With over 1000 citations from scientific journals and ancient texts, and with buckets of ayahuasca, we take on the dualism that has carved black-and-white categories from our richly toned universe: true and false, good and evil, sense and nonsense, illness and health, and lawful and illegal. With metaphors mixed, whipped, folded and stretched, this work is roundabout and back again, silly and sublime, spot on and plain wrong. There are oblique tangents, impassioned rants, endless digressions, bigoted conclusions and thinly veiled provocations. There are also strange cults, venerable sages, wild women, robotic policemen, and eccentrics of various stripes – like my poor messianic friend, whose epiphany at 15,000 feet was snatched up and hurled mercilessly onto the page as a counterpoint. Like him, what I offer is enthusiastic to the point of excess, unabashedly apocalyptic, and ultimately indecent; but my flight of fancy should return you safely and cleanly to the ground.

This book is the story of the apocalypse – how it unfolds in our world, in our history and in our brains. It is written in the faith that revelation is open to everyone, and in the hope that we will embrace it before... but no, this is not that type of apocalyptic book. The Messiah, the Mahdi, the Maitreya is here already, one of 330,000,003 personalities in our schizophrenic heads, serene amongst the bickering. He won't fly in on a cloud, bearded and iridescent and holding a sickle; nor on a plane, bearded and smelly, holding his knob. Science recognises him as a schizophrenic delusion, and even my old rabbi preferred not to talk about him; but he is there, in the mysteries of nature and the depths of our brains. He is there in our scriptures, for those who read between the lines. He is beyond the boundaries of polite conversation, and beyond the range of normal perception; but he is with us all the same.

You may say I'm a dreamer ... ooh ooh ooh.

On pronouns:

English grammar, unfortunately perhaps, insists that something alive be either *he* or *she*, reflecting and perpetuating the dualism wired into our brains. I could use *s/he* and *hir*, of course; but pronouns should be pronounceable, almost by definition, and I'm not sure I can get my tongue around *thim*. If it is any consolation, my wife's native tongue is even more twisted. When I'm going out to see a friend, my Latina wants to know if it is *una amiga* or *un amigo*.

English speakers are spared these concerns (unless we marry them, of course) but our pronouns and our chauvinism still make for some very silly scripture, such as King Solomon's sweet nothings to his beloved God. 'His eyes are as the eyes of doves by the rivers… his lips like lilies, dropping sweet smelling myrrh… yea, he is altogether lovely'.[5]

Is this really what the patriarch had in mind?

1. The Blunt Edge of Ockham's Razor

For Rani Viva, Nemu's midwife

> It is futile to do with more things that which can be done with fewer

> *Brother William of Ockham*[1]

On my first and only trip to Bavaria, I was pleased to wander into a street named Occamstrasse, in honour of the Godfather of the Scientific Method. There was Occam Taxis (presumably driving via the most direct route), an Occam supermarket (perhaps with only essential groceries), and an Occam pub (where they might siphon alcohol directly from keg to stomach). The very idea of drinking made me feel sick though, on that day. Oktoberfest had nearly destroyed me two days previously.

It was all good fun to begin with – men with curvy sausages and Fräuleins bearing beer jugs – but after following a call of nature, I returned into the tent of three thousand shouting, singing Bavarians, stamping on tables and clanging tankards, and I had no idea where my table was. I wandered in circles amongst the pretzels, and never found my friends, but I did find some funny Italians. 'Do you feel a-lika-skinnin-up?' they asked. The rest of Oktoberfest was a barely lucid dream set to *oompah* music; I didn't see another friendly face until I peeled myself off the floor the next morning.

Brother William of Ockham Abbey would have made a beeline back to his table. Back in the fourteenth century, the monk proposed that a question be answered with the simplest explanation possible. This is often formally paraphrased as:

entia non sunt multiplicanda praeter necessitatem

(entities must not be multiplied beyond necessity)[2]

It seems fair enough, but Ockham's razor caused havoc in the Vatican, over the question of apostolic poverty. While the friars of the Franciscan order followed the example of the apostles, and lived as beggars without private property, the Pope was the largest real-estate owner in the known world, and the question arose as to which was the correct Christian lifestyle. Brother William was called over from England to adjudicate. He drew his razor to cut through the complexity, and found, to his surprise, that his beloved Pope was at fault. Moreover the Pope was 'stubbornly heretical',[3] maintaining his heresy even after it had been explained to him. This, according to the monk, disqualified him from the esteemed office of the holy hat. Ockham spent four years under house arrest, fled to Munich and was excommunicated for apostasy; but his principle of simplicity became one of the cornerstones of science. It keeps us from getting lost amidst twisting tunnels of theory.

Some 300 years later, Galileo looked up at the same old sky and saw something new. In the cosmology of the era, Man stood firm on Earth at the centre of Creation, and the planets looped around him in curly-whirly epicycles against the backdrop of the fixed stars. Galileo saw through the scheme. He took Ockham's bread-knife to the pretzels, and made a fresh set of bagels from the planetary orbits. In the realm of ideas, all he did was nudge the sun to the centre, but it was blasphemy for the old hats of the old cosmos.

The first Christian to propose this model was Copernicus, in 1543, but only on his deathbed. Giordano Bruno burned at the stake in 1600 for defending the heresy. But Galileo felt confident, for he revealed what had previously been hidden, with a nautical device he doctored and turned towards the night sky. For the first time in history, the moons of Jupiter came into focus, stubbornly heretical heavenly bodies orbiting something other than Earth. But Catholic cosmologists found fault with the new-fangled device. Their model, indeed the Creator Himself, placed Earth at the centre of the universe (according to their theology, though the Bible has nothing to say on the matter, and the geocentric universe is pure, unadulterated Aristotle). Galileo was a devout Catholic with no reformist agenda, but the Inquisition forbade him from teaching his model, and he died under house arrest. Why the extreme reaction?

We use our theories to grasp the world. Do we ignore a crazy man, or incarcerate him? Do we reason with him or listen to him? Does he need lithium, or needles in his meridians,

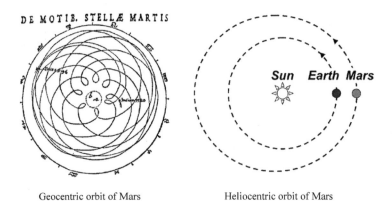

Geocentric orbit of Mars   Heliocentric orbit of Mars

or electrodes across his brain? Does he need an exorcist? It depends on our theory of madness. Theories are the hands of the mind, with which we grapple with problems. A radical new perspective, if it proves to be persuasive, forces a culture to redefine itself, to question its assumptions. Galileo's detractors would not sit back and allow mankind to be pushed from centre stage. Many people prefer their half-baked pretzels to freshly baked bagels, but eventually they must be ejected. After the blur of Oktoberfest, the streets are awash with vomit. My hangover lasted for two days. The ban on Galileo's book lasted over two centuries, and a rather tardy Vatican finally cleared him of any wrongdoing in 1992.

Ockham would have loved his adopted hometown, where the people go straight to the point. When you ask a Bavarian '*Sprekenzi Englischer*?' in a shameful approximation of his language, he might respond with a frown and a '*nein, ich spreche Deutsche.*' No frills, and no messing around. All a party needs is trombones, leather shorts, and beer by the litre. *Prost!* Ockham would have made a great English drunk at Oktoberfest, swaying and scowling, cursing into the sleeve of his habit as the pontiff pontificates in front of the *Fräuleins*, and his whole know-it-all air starts to get the monk's goat. He eyeballs the Pope across the beer tent and nods towards the table football.

The Pope calmly drains his glass of red and accepts the challenge, and the ultimate dream team approaches the table. Magellan fashions a ball from a beer-mat and rolls it into play. The Pope knocks it upfield, but Galileo takes control at the back line and sends it past the Pope's strikers to Newton. The two old virgins eye each other for a furtive moment as Newton's fingers tickle his abacus under the table. He passes to Kant with startling precision as the Pope spins poles wildly. Kant gazes at the table and then calmly kicks the ball to the corner, where it comes to a gradual stop at the edge of the Milky Way. The Pope starts shaking the table and muttering incantations, and

Ockham's quick eyes dart around the tent and fall on Einstein, enjoying a pipe at the bar. Einstein strikes a match, and the table jumps up and flips into a sphere. The Pope recoils shrieking, hat tumbling as Einstein smiles his goofy smile, but the monk glares back. 'I'm off to play dice with God,' he growls. He clinks glasses with Schrödinger, downs his pint, and burps a foul, mathematical cloud of gas on his way out.*

Ockham's razor cuts away, but it gives nothing back. The monk just takes your beloved beliefs outside and gives them a good kicking. Medieval cosmologists did not know how God pushed the planets round. Newton knew no better:

> I have not been able to discover the cause of those properties of gravity from the phenomena, and I frame no hypothesis; for whatever is not deduced from the phenomena is to be called an hypothesis; and hypotheses, whether metaphysical or physical, whether of occult qualities or mechanical, have no place in experimental philosophy.[4]

Today's most advanced hypothesis on gravity requires a purely hypothetical particle called a graviton, for which no evidence exists. In the absence of reliable knowledge, models are born, they develop and compete, and they are killed; but they never become true. They become superstitions. The theoretician, a different beast from the experimental philosopher, is counselled by Karl Popper to accept models only provisionally. Popper called this falsificationism, and took it almost word for word from Newton:

---

* 1519: Magellan sets sail on the first circumnavigation of the globe.
  1632: Galileo publishes *Dialogue Concerning the Two Chief World Systems.*
  1755: Kant publishes *Universal Natural History and Theory of the Heavens* proposing that the Milky Way is one of many galaxies in the universe.
  1915: Einstein publishes his general theory of relativity
  1933: Schrödinger suggests that matter is a function of probability density.

In experimental philosophy [said Newton] we are to look upon propositions collected by general induction from phenomena as accurately or very nearly true, notwithstanding any contrary hypotheses that may be imagined, 'till such time as other phenomena occur.[5]

What is knowledge anyway? It is not a physical thing; but neither is it a metaphysical ideal, like a perfect circle that can never be drawn, a mathematical constant with an infinite decimal tail, or a goddess of sublime beauty who never ages. Knowledge, eventually, relates to nothing but itself, and leads nowhere but back to itself:

What is sugar?

A sweet, white, crystalline substance.

What does white look like?

Like snow and sugar lumps.

What does sweet taste like?

Like sugar.

We are none the wiser until we know sugar intimately, until our tongues taste it and our teeth fall out, after which wordy descriptions are redundant. The same is true for any proposition one can make. In the final analysis, it refers to an experience that reveals the 'suchness' of a thing. The revelation might be our own, or it might be someone else's, in which case we place our faith in their judgement. Otherwise, we must admit our ignorance.

We move the planets and the goalposts, but can we be sure they will stay where we put them? The sun rises in the east, but how do we know it will obey the same law tomorrow?† Can we be sure of anything?

'Can you bollocks!' bellows Ockham, urinating against the Pearly Gates.

---

† Einstein endorsed a theory that it might not, discussed in *Apocalypses Past, Present and Personal.*

What are we composed of? Ask a physiologist and it would be cells and sinews, whereas an artist might picture you as line and light. A Freudian might describe urges and neuroses, and an economist demands and means; but who knows? Knowledge is a bubbling cauldron of meaning, suspended over the abyss on invisible strands of nothingness. Knowledge always boils down to nothing – which is not a problem in itself, but we invariably confuse subjective knowledge for objective reality. We think we have worked something out, so we stop thinking about it, and forget that the map is not the territory, and the territory is not *terra firma*. The menu is not the food, so mind you don't choke on laminated cardboard. Theories are tools, not truths. Ockham preferred the simplest tool for the job, and partly thanks to him we have a fantastic toolbox; but the raw material of life is something different. To cross the abyss to the infinite, knowledge must be left behind.

Charles Fort could 'conceive of nothing, in religion, science or philosophy, that is more than the proper thing to wear, for a while.'[6] Etymologically speaking, philosophy is the love (*philo*) of Sophia, the goddess of intimate knowledge. Hers is the knowledge which comes from inspiration, not from books. Philosophy should be like making love to a goddess, but the word has come to refer to a set of beliefs used to judge the world and organise your life. For example, your philosophy may be Marxism, or maybe it is the Golden Rule, doing unto others as you would have them do unto you. Very good, think what thou wilt; but too often we get lost in our definitions and identifications, and we forget the lovely Sophia. Philosophy liberates. 'A' philosophy binds. 'A' philosophy ultimately fails in the real world – when a sadomasochist applies his version of the Golden Rule to your nipples, or a Marxist finds herself in a room full of horny men on Viagra, obliged to give according to her abilities to each according to his needs.

Ω

We often claim to live by some kind of philosophy when we are in fact philosophising by some kind of life, weaving some makeshift garment to cover our habits and desires. By way of illustration, allow me to introduce a seeker I met at the feet of an extraordinary *sadhu*. This ash-clad holy man had raised his hand aloft over 20 years previously in devotion to Shiva, and left it to mortify into place, with hideous nails curling downwards. I could hardly refuse a toot on this holy man's 'Kali chillum' (which was, after all, one of his only possessions, besides his mobile and his Rolex). As I exhaled, I noticed said seeker. We exchanged pleasantries as I coughed, and he told me he'd spent 26 years wandering around India, visiting saints and sages.

At this point a nearby *sadhu* asked if I was married, as Indians are wont to do, even those who have renounced such fetters as wives. 'No, but I have a Japanese girlfriend,' I replied, pushing my nose flat and saying *'chota naak'*, thereby exhausting my Hindi vocabulary. The ascetics creased up laughing, but the seeker looked blankly at me, so I told him *'chota naak'* and pressed my *naak* flat. He shrugged his shoulders mournfully. He didn't know the word for 'nose' in Hindi. He didn't know any Hindi at all.

Perhaps I was in no position to judge, having practically exhausted my vocabulary already. But

Photo courtesy of Bennett Stevens

25

though I reached for a state of *samadhi* beyond judgement, my holy-hash mashed mush must have betrayed me, as he began to justify himself. 'I have purposely not learnt any Hindi, lest the verbal interfere with my spiritual experience of the *sadhus*.'

This is a philosophy, clearly, something to wear for a while, but this malodorous tie-dye rag has grown so crusty that it restricts his movement. Better to go naked like the *naga babas*, and mortify something less vital than your cerebral cortex! At least his garment covers nothing more sinister than laziness. A *mafioso* sees a dog-eat-dog world because he wants to eat other dogs. Nazi theorists reasoned that the Sudetenland was theirs because they wanted it. This philosophising has nothing to do with love, nor Sophia.

Our scientific beliefs are a laundry bag of second-hand rags cut to resemble lab coats, dyed in the distillate of our prejudices. To a great extent, they are given to us, not chosen by us; but they define our world and set the limits of acceptable belief and behaviour. Stray too far, and one might be ridiculed, or even incarcerated.

Back when philosophers still knew how to make Sophia shudder, Socrates sought wisdom from the wise. The poets, priests and politicians he asked knew a few things about a few things, concluded Socrates, but their faith in their incomplete knowledge blinkered them. Socrates maintained his ignorance, and the Oracle at Delphi judged him to be the wisest of men, as he at least knew his own ignorance. The state judged him to be a corrupter of the young, and executed him.

Ignorance is a good start, but if knowledge is empty and nothing we can say about the world is true, what are we to believe in? Ockham believed in God, and considered any other rigidly held belief to be an obstacle to his grace. Today's seekers are more sceptical, and with good reason. God and the devil have been used as umbrella terms to explain things beyond our ken, as shields against uncertainty. In the beginning, God created

Heaven and Earth; he caused the rain to fall and the belly to swell; but as our understanding broadened, the unknown shrank and scientists moved in on God's territory. Jealous medieval gods are fighting a reactionary counter-attack, burning down abortion clinics and chasing Darwin from schools in the US.[7] But Richard Dawkins, ayatollah of a new church, answers with bombast, pointing cameras at rabid fundamentalists to prove that religion is the root of all evil. In his theology, religion is a mind virus caught from one's parents; but he is talking about doctrines, taboos, guilty urges and hand-me-down maps of the universe – the outer trappings of religion. The inner, esoteric traditions are something else.

For Gnostics, there was and is more to God than the unknown: the divine can be known directly through a process of gnosis, through dreams, insights, trance and sudden revelation. Church fathers have militated against such ideas since the third century, and continue to insist that God still moves in zones beyond our understanding. A miracle cure is recognised by the Vatican, therefore, 'when there is no remaining possibility of a natural explanation'.[8] (In other words, if we can explain it scientifically, it is not a miracle; and if we can't, it is.)

In 1882, Nietzsche announced that God was dead, and the thinking man breathed a sigh of relief.[9] The modern scientist may not invoke God in her theories. The eternal questions remain, but without the Holy Inquisition and eternal damnation to worry about, our scope to think is broader.

Meanwhile the established faiths have fallen on hard times, rent by schisms and shamed by child-molesters. For the spiritually minded, Buddhism offers superior techniques, Taoism funnier stories, and Rasta funkier bass-lines, outcompeting pallid priests, reactionary imams, wheeler-dealer Brahmins and nitpicking rabbis who commit the ultimate blasphemy of making God boring. It doesn't matter if you are a tangled beard of orthodoxy or a well-trimmed liberal mincing

about the pulpit: if you represent the divine, then surely it should lend you some charisma (from *kharis* meaning 'divine grace'). But old-school monotheism, with its moralism and its dirges, is like a frail old man wheeled out for christenings and funerals, breathing softly through the mucus as he dreams of the good old days.

Many bemoan the loss of faith and morality, but in some ways we are closer to God today than ever before. A mind full of cobwebs and mumbo-jumbo is no good to anyone; but with razor in hand, the seeker is free to follow ideas wherever they wander, beyond the puke and the pretzels, beyond the bagels, and eventually beyond the confines of the beer tent. We have incredible resources at our fingertips: science journals, lecture courses, translated scriptures from all over the world, meditation classes, devotional music to download, therapies, workshops, and a plethora of sects, from ayahuasca to Zen.

Novices once pounded on the gate of the Zen monastery for days before being allowed in. Yoga, Kabbalah and Latin were restricted to certain classes of men. Magickal secrets were buried in code, but today the hidden is revealed, and online. The acolyte need only put aside business, laziness and TV, and burrow through the layers of half-truth and half-witted commentary caked over the teachings. But if he (or even she, for the first time in a long time) is as persistent as the Zen monks of old, the libraries are open. She can believe what she likes, or believe nothing at all, and God is entirely optional. As Rabbi David Cooper puts it in his excellent *God is a Verb*:

> What is God? In a way, there is no God. Our perception of God usually leads to a misunderstanding that seriously undermines our spiritual development.[10]

Even if she has swallowed the narcotics of materialism, the lonely vacuum of atheism is far less stifling to the mind than the fiery lakes of hell, and she needn't fear thumbscrews, excommunication, or death, unless she is careless enough to go and do a Rushdie.

Before the Reformation, if you disagreed with the church there was nowhere else to turn, you couldn't just don a skullcap and gatecrash a synagogue. Despite this, Brother William went against convention and the immense power of the Pope, losing his liberty and risking his life. What would drive him to attack the Pope he once believed to be infallible?

Only love drives drunks to reject their drinking partners. Ockham did not believe in God as a theory. He loved God as reality permeating the universe, in the revealed and the hidden, at the beginning and at the end. His divine was more intimate than words and theories, more important than politics and material concerns, including his own safety. He was looking in on the illusion from outside. The razor is only part of the story. Trading insults at the bar is only part of the story. After an evening arguing with fools, Ockham returns home to the monastery and changes from belligerent drunk into affectionate lover, reciting poems to his beloved, staying up all night to be near his beloved, praising his beloved before and after every meal.

Over the millennia, monks from Shaolin to Santiago de Compostela developed a range of meditative techniques. They did not observe vows of poverty and silence for kicks, and pray through long vigils or sit shivering under waterfalls because they had nothing better to do. These are the techniques of ecstasy (*ex-* 'out' + *histanai* 'to stand'), a state available to anyone sincerely devoted to getting out of their heads, and exploring beyond their boundaries.

Since the dawn of civilisation, people have been praying, singing, sacrificing, and confessing to something invisible; but recently, we have decided collectively that there is nothing more to life than the tiny slice that fits on a microscope slide. Materialistic culture rejects mystical techniques and experiences with tremendous arrogance. If scientific paths to wisdom are so much better, then why all the imperfection in our scientific world?

Meditation has all but fallen away in the Judeo-Christian tradition. Humming along at church on the odd Sunday lacks the depth of the traditional monastic meditations, and Madonna is far more into Kabbalah than most Jews I know (including the rabbis). Many seekers prefer to go east, to the daddy of godless metaphysics. The Buddha taught more psychology than religion, and he did it without walking on water or knobbing thousands of milkmaids. At the centre of the story is a normal man at his wits end, sitting under a tree and refusing to move until he had sorted it out. Freed from the tyranny of the gods, Buddhists developed techniques for exploring the immense scope of the inner world. Though the cosmology admits plenty of deities, even 'garlanded with black serpents and fresh skulls', they are recognised as 'the form of your own mind',[11] along with everything else in the universe. The evidence of one's own senses is paramount:

> Do not go upon... tradition; nor upon rumor; nor upon
> what is in a scripture; ... nor upon another's seeming
> ability; nor upon the consideration, 'The monk is
> our teacher.' ... When you yourselves know: 'These
> things... lead to harm and ill,' abandon them.[12]

With this sentiment in mind, the Dalai Lama at a talk I attended poked fun at Buddhist scriptures describing the sun as a few feet across. The Pope, by contrast, does not ridicule creationist accounts of six days of Creation. Faith is serious business in Catholicism.

Of course, the sublime Buddha-mind without opinion is not easily attainable, so the Buddha recommends non-attachment as a steppingstone on the way. Opinions are employed as needed, and ditched when something better arises. This ancient doctrine, which closely resembles falsificationism, quietly draws us away from the drunken brawls of the beer tent.

Meditation is also a most scientific of disciplines, and its results are more directly knowable than anything in the mundane sciences. A chemist observes a colour change in a beaker and a moving needle on a thermometer. She infers that heat has been produced and a compound formed, and from there speculates further into the acts of the particles involved, but what is an ion other than a speck of speculation swimming in wavy gravy? All a scientist actually knows is that the needle moves, or that data fills a computer page.

With meditation, the jumpy needles of the technician's own perceptual apparatus gradually settle, and the page becomes blank. Repeat investigations gradually develop focus, balance and calm, and the technician also finds herself cushioned from the stress of burnt toast and other everyday irritations. There may be no great revelation, but who ever found the meaning of life inside a test tube? Scientific theories, though fascinating and useful, have also been used to justify the oppression of women and various races, and sometimes the fruits of science contaminate rivers for decades. Science cultivates data and knowledge, but not necessarily the wisdom to use it.

If the seeker perseveres, however, then one day, quite suddenly as she pours a cup of tea or glances out of the window, she may find that the world suddenly melts into harmonious unity. This happened to me during a dinner party in Japan with my Aikido class, as my friend leaned forward to take a piece of meat from the grill. Somehow the tremor of his chopsticks, his stuttering speech and general nervous disposition came together, along with the quiet air of authority surrounding sensei at the head of the table, the smell of the food, the sound of two young karaoke crooners in the background, and everyone and everything there, including the straw mats, the sliding doors, and including me. It all blended into a scene of transcendental normality. For about two minutes, I chewed on a grilled pepper in a state of complete bliss, high as a kite but totally present. It was one of the strangest things that ever happened to me. Yet nothing happened.

This experience is not unusual; it happens to non-meditators as well, and it is momentous. Our piecemeal theories become less binding after glimpsing the cosmic dance-floor, where everything moves to the pulse of the universe under the party lights of the Milky Way, where every agent is a disco dancer getting their groove on, with continental plates traversing the floor in a slo-mo tango, seasons switching the visuals, protons and electrons spinning in clinches of desperate affinity, strands of DNA swapping juicy secrets, doing the twist again and again and again. This moment is a philosopher's stone, which transmutes every mundane experience into gold. From then onwards, nothing can ever be the same again. I stepped up to sing another Carpenters classic a completely new man.

The highest goal of mundane science is a theory to bring together everything in the universe. Newton's theory of gravity was the first universal principle, governing apples falling at the local scale and planets orbiting at the astronomical. Newton, however, was no mundane scientist. He practised the forbidden art of alchemy, and only managed to avoid trouble by keeping a lifelong 'high silence' concerning it.[13] *As above, so below* was, for him, a familiar mystical formula relating the microcosm to the macrocosm. He simply reformulated it as a physical law.

Galileo Galilee, whose very name is an opera of extravagance, kept no high silence, and died under house arrest. Such outspoken pioneers rarely escape controversy, because the mind that devotes itself to the order of the beer tent is a political mind, which slots into positions of power behind the bar, comfortable to be serving another round of the usual to the regulars.

Ockham's razor cuts through our models. Some mourn as their edifices crumble; but for the open-eyed and uninvested, all that is lost is that which lies between them and deeper understanding. In life, the razor can reveal opportunities. In science, it became the first rule, as restated by Newton:

> We are to admit no more causes of natural things, than such as are both true and sufficient to explain their appearances.[14]

Science grows along the wound made by Ockham's razor, but truly revolutionary ideas rarely result from beavering away in labs, tapping at computers and totting up tables. Revelation comes when the rational mind is bypassed in dreams, trances and sudden insights, as we will see in the following chapter. The rational mind wields the razor to choose between models, but this is secondary to the creative, non-rational processes of the unconscious, which generate the models in the first place. Some of the models we will be considering in this book are unorthodox, even unpopular, but let us set aside theory for a while. We can suspend our disbelief (or rather, our belief), and focus on how things happen in the real world, beneath the layers of meaning and interpretation.

For the immoderate amongst us, drunken with dogma, Ockham's razor is wielded without finesse. Rather than slashing the ropes of the tent to reveal, we remain at the bar, fighting amongst ourselves as we down theory after theory, toasting our potency and getting lost whenever nature calls. Look closely into the dregs in your glass. The kegs are running dry and spitting foam. The bell for last orders rang decades ago. The lights are flicking on and off, and a nasty hangover is brewing. It is time to drag our sorry selves back home, and have a good think about what we have been doing.

2. KILLER CREEDS AND DIRTY DEEDS

To Sammy, licking plates clean in dog heaven.

'AUM MANI PADME HUM'

Avalokiteshvara

'WOOF, WOOF-WOOF WOOF-WOOF-WOOF!'

Sammy

'As I write, highly civilised human beings are flying overhead, trying to kill me.'[1]

George Orwell

'WOOF, WOOFITY WOOF-WOOF WOOF'

Sammy

My friend's dog Hempy was an eye-clawing, shirt-tearing, computer-licking monster. He was all animal, no human social protocols at all, and his master was only slightly better house-trained. We were once invited to a harvest festival in Yoshino village, where two distinct groups were celebrating: organic farmers in wellies, and beardy Rastas in big hats. For some reason, Yoshino houses a number of Orientals who claim the divinity of Haile Selassie, who cook fish tea and *ackee*, and who have invested years into forcing their straight hair into unconvincing dreadlocks. Perhaps the mystique of the unfamiliar worked on them, in the same way that it inspired a Jamaican reggae star to choose the name Ninja Man. (In a complicated reciprocation, there is now a Japanese dancehall DJ calling himself Nanja Man.)

After a day of wholesome harvest feasting, the bong-heads sneaked off to sample a different harvest. The boss Rasta skinned up solidly for three hours before dropping his pace. Less disciplined was Hempy, who broke his leash and attacked a smaller dog by the name of Ganja. Ganja never stood a chance.

No doubt there was some important pheromonal issue at stake. From my perspective, however, they were just dogs fighting. From a dog's eye view, fighting the infidel or to liberate the oppressed, fighting for anything other than bones and boning would mean nothing at all.

Dogs are slaves to their noses, driven wild by a bitch in heat; but with their noses to the ground they cause much less trouble than we monkeys. They almost never kill each other, but we who are slaves to our concepts regularly kill strangers en masse for wearing different uniforms and thinking different thoughts. We are rewarded for it with medals. Lemmings occasionally kill themselves by mistake, when their migration instinct is confused, but we do it on purpose during existential crises. Meaning is a powerful force. Three words can suddenly change everything:

'I love you.'

'Ready... Aim... Fire!'

No dog ever claimed more land than he could perfume. There was no canine King Philip of Spain and Jerusalem. We are far more territorial than dogs, but unlike dogs we rationalise our greed and pursue total dominion.

In 1492, a small Spanish force took the blessing of the Pope and sailed off for the New World. The natives they met knew nothing of the holy book that held Europe under its sway, nor of the magick of steel. Columbus noted:

> They do not bear arms, and do not know them for I showed them a sword – they took it by the edge and cut themselves.[2]

Conquistadors arrive in South America

Along with steel and zeal, gunpowder helped reduce the native population of Hispaniola, the first new World colony, by a third in four years, to 200,000. Fifty years later, a cleric doubted whether 500 remained, and this stirred him to poetry:

> To use gunpowder against pagans is to offer incense to the Lord.[3]

Old World disease also played its part, and was interpreted as the hand of the Lord decimating the heathen before the conquistadors.[4]

Things were more complicated for North American pioneers a century later. They were mostly Protestants, for whom divine authority humbug reeked of the Antichrist Pope. They preferred to rationalise the land-grab:

> These savages have no particular propriety in any part or parcel of that country, but only a general residency there, as wild beasts in the forest; for they range and wander up and down the country without any law or government, being led only by their own lusts and sensuality. There is not *meum* and *tuum* [mine and thine] amongst them. So that if the whole land should be taken from them, there is not a man that can complain of any particular wrong done unto him.[5]

Today there are large Indian populations in South and Central America. Aztec, Mayan and Inca blood runs thick in Latin American veins, but the few North American tribes that survived are largely confined to their reservations, and so is their DNA. Why were Protestants so much more skilled at genocide than Catholics?

The main theological difference between the Spanish devils and the pale-faced pilgrims of the Mayflower was the matter of transubstantiation. A Catholic, especially a sixteenth-century Catholic, was led to believe that something occurred under the consecrated hands of the priest during Mass, *turning* the bread and wine into the body and blood of Christ. More sober-minded

Protestants understood the bread and wine _to symbolise_ the body and blood. Catholics still keep it real, venerating splinters from the cross and filings from St. Peter's chains in their churches, sometimes carrying plastic fetishes in the form of Mary-shaped bottles of holy water with screw-top heads.

Roman Catholicism is a romantic and raw affair, where demons are exorcised, confession is made and penitence is pay. Protestantism is far more sophisticated and sensible; rituals are sober, churches are more austere. The flock is expected to read and discuss _The Bible_, rather than listen to scary stories about saints with spears in their eyes or worms wriggling in their flesh. Conquistadors expected to find a terrestrial paradise in the New World, where Judas went for his annual holiday from Hell, with mermaids and wonderful animals, with trees hung with jewels and gold everywhere.[6] The Puritan pioneers planned to build New Jerusalem themselves, and that is far more disruptive.

The Spanish and Portuguese took their abstract construction (the Catholic church) west with a zealous agenda, but somewhere

Puritans arrive in North America

along the line their resolve softened. Perhaps they fell in love, as Mediterraneans are wont to do. From the beginning, they had a soft spot for the native, as Columbus reveals:

> They are the best people in the world and above all
> the gentlest – without knowledge of what is evil – they
> do not murder or steal … they love their neighbours
> as themselves … They would make fine servants. With
> fifty men we could subjugate them all and make them
> do whatever we want.[7]

As well as deporting 'in the name of the Holy Trinity, as many slaves as could be sold',[8] Catholics converted their charges. They also took lovers, beginning with Cortez himself who fell in love with his interpreter. The Indian soon came to be seen as a 'natural child' to be educated.[9] Natives, newcomers and their African slaves mixed traditions and genes, producing beautiful religious art, cracking music, and some stunning women a few hundred years down the line. They also left all sorts of funky theological syncretisms, including Voodoo, Santería, Candomblé, and a thread leading to Daime, of which we will hear more.

Puritan pioneers carried an even more abstract construction, that was not only symbolic but cognisant of the symbolism. They took their *super*-abstract conception to the New World and took over. Moved by the frontier spirit rather than the Holy Spirit, and less interested in poking Pocahontas, they barely mixed, and they did not convert. They ensured the Indian had a steady supply of whisky, and practiced their genocide with scientific precision, exterminating buffalo herds, force-marching Indians to barren land, advancing civilisation by making treaties with the illiterate.

The Declaration of Independence of 1776 marks the birth of humanistic politics. North Americans turned against the divinely sanctioned king in favour of 'the authority of the good people of these colonies'. God himself became a rationalist:

> We hold these truths to be self-evident, that all men are
> created equal, that they are endowed by their Creator
> with certain unalienable rights, that among these are
> life, liberty and the pursuit of happiness.[10]

This historic document, however, signed 150 years after
the first pioneers landed, included a clause justifying their
tense relations with 'the inhabitants of our frontiers, the
merciless Indian savages, whose known rule of warfare is an
undistinguished destruction of all ages, sexes and conditions.'[11]
By contrast, only 21 years after Catholics made landfall, the
Pope declared that savages must be considered human beings,
and later began excommunicating slavers who dared to
subjugate them.[12]

In the north, the United State of Mind was made up, and
the decision stuck for centuries. When Senator Henry Dawes
visited the Cherokee Nation in the 1880s, the comments he
made carried the echo of *meum* and *tuum*:

> there was not a family in that whole nation that had
> not a home of its own... not a pauper... it built its own
> schools and hospitals. Yet the defect of the system
> was apparent. They have got as far as they can go,
> because they own their land in common... here is not
> enterprise to make your home any better than that of
> your neighbours. Here is no selfishness, which is at the
> bottom of civilisation.[13]

The first nation to be founded upon the ideals of rationalism
practiced slavery long after divinely sanctioned kings and Popes
had abandoned it. Racial segregation was legally sanctioned
until the 1970s, and black ghettoes and Indian reservations are
still the poorest zones of the US.

It has been suggested that warfare is a disease of the developed
nations, because pre-Columbian skeletons have fewer wounds
resulting from violence than post-Columbian generations.[14]
But war may be a matter of degree. The Lakota were fighting
other tribes before they fought the white man (though it may

41

be misleading to equate a cattle raid with warfare). It seems that the more developed the abstract function grows, the more destructive we become.

'Capitalist rationality does not do away with sub- or super-rational impulses,' wrote Joseph Schumpeter, the great economist. 'It merely makes them get out of hand by removing the restraint of sacred or semi-sacred tradition.'[15] Irrational impulses are tooled up with weapons and technologies that would have boggled the mind of the most romantic of conquistadors. From the perspective of the forgotten braves buried under the American prairies, where the *meum* of a modern cowboy might be a ranch bigger than England, our animal desires and the limitations of our flesh would have been entirely preferable.

Our philosophies, our technologies, our nuclear submarines and monuments might impress us, but dogs piss on our monuments without a second thought, as the monk pisses in the temple in the Zen tale.[16] To both the Buddha mind and the canine mind, it is just piss on a rock. Only the everyday human mind, half-awake between the two, is alarmed by the symbolism.

A healthy dog navigates his smelly world, sniffing and secreting as he goes. A happy human roams the abstract. Our minds produce the sweet flowers of the arts, the sharp thorns of etiquette, the soft grass of banter, and the choking vines of bureaucracy. Everything grows in this shitbag of a brain; so if we must have philosophies, and we may be neurologically obliged to, we should at least keep them pruned and responsibly composted, so as not to ruin the garden. After all, even the dumbest dog knows not to soil his own kennel.

Ω

3. THE GENIUS OF SCIENCE

To my granny

Let us learn to dream, gentlemen, then perhaps we shall find the truth.[1]

Friedrich August Kekulé

As the sun set over Budapest in 1882, Nicola Tesla was reciting poetry with a friend, when he was suddenly struck by a vision: a new machine hung before him with all the clarity of metal. It was the AC motor, which powers our national grids today.[2]

It is difficult to imagine the planet without the hundreds of patents Tesla took, including technologies fundamental to computing, robotics, and radio and telecommunications. He demonstrated wireless electrical transmission by lighting lamps 25 miles away, and discovered both terrestrial standing waves and cosmic waves, which he claimed could be converted into free electricity.

Portrait of Tesla in his lab

Tesla made neither blueprints nor calculations for his intricate machines. He simply lay down on the couch:

> I saw new scenes. These were at first blurred and indistinct and would flit away when I tried to concentrate my attention on them. They gained strength and distinctness and finally assumed the concreteness of real things… Every night, and sometimes during the day… I would start on my journeys, see new places, cities and countries… I needed no models, drawing or experiments. I could picture them all as real in my mind.[3]

Tesla was the ultimate comic-book mad genius, with an enormous antenna emerging from his lab, and homemade electrical storms and explosions terrifying his neighbours. He was also obsessive (about hygiene and the number three), and compulsive (always eating the same meal with the same number of peas, at the same table in the same restaurant, cleaning his cutlery with eighteen napkins).[4]

Genius tends to be associated with madness; one Dr. Lombroso commented, in all seriousness, that 'genius is a symptom of hereditary degeneration of the epileptoid variety, and is allied to moral insanity.'[5] The classical conception was different. In Latin, one's *genius* is the spirit who brought ideas from another plane (pictured in the Roman mosic on page 43). Everyone had their own personal *genius*, a distinct entity with its own personality; and on their birthdays Romans offered sacrifices to the spirits that made them think. It makes me think, anyway. It makes me wonder who the candles on my birthday cake are for.

Genius comes through the veil into consciousness in various ways. For Henri Poincaré, who laid the foundations of chaos mathematics, ideas came 'in the morning or evening in bed while in a semi-hypnagogic state.'[6] The structural theory in chemistry arose from a vision of dancing atoms that Friedrich August Kekulé had 'one fine summer evening as I was returning by the last omnibus'.[7]

On another occasion

> I was sitting, writing at my textbook; but the work did not progress; my thoughts were elsewhere. I turned my chair toward the fire and dozed. Again the atoms were gambolling before my eyes. This time the smaller groups now kept modestly in the background... But look! What was that? One of the snakes had seized hold of its own tail, and the form whirled mockingly before my eyes.[8]

Kekulé's vision of the oroborous revealed to him the shape of the benzene ring shortly. It also occurred at the point when he abandoned rational thought. Insights emerge into consciousness when the mind disengages, and sometimes with a sort of insistant urgency. Otto Loewi's dream revelation, which would lead to a breakthough in scientific understanding of the nervous system, occurred twice on consecutive nights:

It occurred to me at six o'clock in the morning that during the night I had written down something important, but I was unable to decipher the scrawl. The next night, at three o'clock the idea returned. It was the design of an experiment to determine whether or not the hypothesis of chemical transmission [of nerve signals] that I had uttered seventeen years ago was correct. I got up immediately, went to the laboratory, and performed a simple experiment on a frog heart... If I had carefully considered it in daytime, I would undoubtedly have rejected the kind of experiment I performed. ... It was good fortune that at the time of the hunch I did not think but acted.[9]

Albert Einstein retired in a familiar state of nervous confusion one night after a day of fruitless brainstorming, only to awake 'as if a storm broke loose in my mind.'[10] After a few weeks of frantic scribbling, he mailed off his paper and returned to bed exhausted, having dismantled the foundations of Newtonian physics with his theory of special relativity.

'Inspiration' once referred to a spirit 'breathing in' to a person (*in* 'in' + *spire* 'to breathe'). For Srinivasa Ramanujan, a totally self-trained Indian mathematician, the spirit was his family goddess, who spoke through his dreams. Ninety years after his death, his (or her) mathematical theorems have spawned whole subdisciplines of maths, and are employed in string theory.[11] 'An equation for me has no meaning', he once remarked, 'unless it represents a thought of God'.[12]

Artists can also be inspired as they doze. Composer Giuseppe Tartini named his *Trillo del Diavolo* for the devil, who played it to him on a fiddle in a dream.[13] Wagner's masterpiece *Rheingold* was produced one afternoon during a feverish bout of insomnia, and Mozart's genius worked best when he was

entirely alone, and of good cheer – say, travelling in a carriage, or walking after a good meal, or during the night when I cannot sleep; ... Whence and how they

> come, I know not; nor can I force them... Nor do I
> hear in my imagination the parts successively but I
> hear them, as it were, all at once. All this inventing,
> this producing, takes place in a pleasing lively dream...
> The committing to paper is done quickly enough, for
> everything is already finished.[14]

Whereas the rational mind plods along step-by-step, inspiration arrives fully formed, or in a continuous stream. Rossini wrote all 600 pages of *The Barber of Seville* in just 13 days. 'He has always been such a lazy fellow,' commented Donizetti, who composed an opera in eight days.[15] William Blake wrote 'from immediate dictation, 12 or sometimes 20 or 30 lines at a time, without premeditation and even against my will.'[16] According to Friedrich Nietzsche, who wrote the first part of his *Thus Spake Zarathustra* in ten days during a debilitating attack of influenza:

> one is the mere incarnation, mouthpiece or medium of an
> almighty power. The idea of revelation in the sense that
> something becomes suddenly visible and audible with
> indescribable certainty and accuracy... with necessity,
> unhesitatingly – I have never had any choice in the
> matter. There is an ecstasy such that the immense strain
> of it is sometimes relaxed by a flood of tears... There
> is the feeling that one is completely out of hand, with
> the very distinct consciousness of an endless number
> of fine thrills and quiverings to the very toes... There is
> an instinct for rhythmic relations... Everything happens
> quite involuntarily, as if in a tempestuous outburst of
> freedom, of absoluteness, of power and divinity. ...
> everything seems to present itself as the readiest, the
> correctest and the simplest means of expression.[17]

Inspiration may also arrive completely unexpected. Melvin Calvin was waiting in a car park when:

> suddenly... in a matter of seconds, the cyclic character
> of the path of carbon became apparent to me... the
> original recognition of phosphoglyceric acid, and how

it got there, and how the acceptor might be regenerated,
all occurred in a matter of 30 seconds.[18]

The Calvin cycle is central to photosynthesis, and it earned
him a Nobel Prize. Carl Gauss's inspiration also arrived out of
nowhere. He suspected that any number can be represented as
a product of its primes in one and only one way, but could not
find the proof. The proof found him four years later:

> but not on account of my painful efforts. Like a sudden
> flash of lightning, the riddle happened to be solved...
> For my part I am unable to name the nature of the
> thread which connected what I previously knew with
> that which made my success possible.[19]

André-Marie Ampère redefined the field of probability and
earned himself a professorship after a similar experience:

> It was seven years ago I proposed to myself a problem
> which I have not been able to solve directly... At last,
> I do not know how, I found it, together with a large
> number of curious and new considerations concerning
> the theory of probability.[20]

The logic circuit, the computer, and the Google search
employ Boolean algebra, a system representing logical
processes as algebraic operations. George Boole considered it
to be the completion of a mission God gave him as a teenager,
to explain how the mind processes thought. The solution came
to him in a flash as he was contemplating mysticism 'from
some source, invisible and undefinable'.[21] Today we might call
that source the *unconscious*.

Sigmund Freud, who first proposed the unconscious, saw
it as the seat of neurosis, a realm dominated by base urges,
without causality, chronology, logic or morality. A scientist
in the rationalist tradition, Freud felt that this unruly shadow
needed to be brought out into the light, controlled and channelled
towards civilised ends under the dominion of the conscious;
and so he originally named it the *sub*conscious. Many later

48

psychoanalysts also sought to 'make the unconscious conscious', but for Milton Erickson it was the creative, healing part of the mind, accessed using hypnosis, shock therapy and confusion. Erickson's own insights, which form the backbone of neurolinguistic programming, often came to him in 'blinding flashes of light'.[22] For Jung, the unconscious was both unlimited and collective, manifesting in dreams,

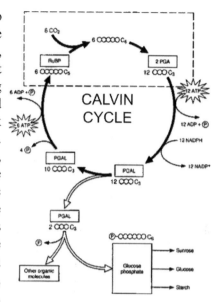

behavioural traits and what he termed *synchronicities* (patterns behind apparently unrelated events that illuminate processes hidden to the conscious mind).

Simultaneous discovery, where two people independently discover something at the same time, is a type of synchronicity, and some of history's most world-changing ideas have broken through the veil like this, as if obeying some impatient agenda. The naturalist Alfred Wallace's revelation came to him on his sickbed, during a malarial fever in the Malay Archipelago.[23] When he had recovered enough to write it up, he sent his work to Charles Darwin, to whom he sometimes sent zoological specimens from his travels. Darwin was horrified to read that Wallace, 14 years his junior, had discovered the principle of the survival of the fittest, and understood its evolutionary consequences, in a matter of three days while sick. Darwin, by contrast, had spent decades studying animal husbandry and comparing specimens, but he hesitated to publish something so shocking to contemporary sensibilities. Wasting no more time, he published the following year. Perhaps his theory would have remained secret otherwise. Newton kept calculus to himself, even covering his mathematical tracks in his publications, until Leibniz discovered it independently ten years later. Heisenberg's uncertainty principle is another simultaneous discovery, which struck psychologist Elton Mayo at the same time. Graham Bell took the patent for the telephone only hours before Elisha Grey submitted a similar device.[24]

Ω

According to Alfred Lord Tennyson, the receptive state occurs when 'individuality itself seemed to dissolve and fade away into boundless being'.[25] The key may be meditation, hypnogogic trance, dream or feverish delirium; but what is the source? Do breakthroughs well up from the depths of the unconscious, or are they carried on the breath of spirits? (Or is the process one and the same?) For Emanuel Swedenborg (1688–1772), the source was Jesus, who appeared in his visions and dreams. Since childhood, Swedenborg meditated on his breath whenever concentrating, and he recorded how angels visited him to teach him techniques of breath control.[26] He also described how the Lord had visited him in London with a mission to reveal hidden things, but this apparently psychotic man was the foremost mineralogist in Europe, who mastered eight languages and filled several library shelves with writings covering diverse subjects from anatomy to geometry to the diameter of the moon. He described a system of forms repeated in nature at different scales, calling to mind the fractals that mathematicians applied to biology and geography centuries later, and he also pre-empted both the wave theory of light and Bell's interconnectedness:

> This universal, including its smallest particles, is a work coherent as a unit, to the extent that no one part can be touched and affected without some sense of it overflowing to all the rest.[27]

He also described the subatomic world:

> The smaller and closer the parts are to the simple
> substratum, the smaller they are in mass, their
> dissimilarities soften, their imperfections decrease and
> their forms become more perfect. They are also lighter
> and quicker in their motion.[28]

Elsewhere he suggested that elementary particles might not exist independently. He conceptualised them as vehicles assumed by energy to get things done, an idea which remains speculative in physics.

Similar conclusions were reached by the Buddha, who also practiced breath meditation. He described the body as a collection of innumerable millions of *kalapas* in perpetual motion and flux, constantly forming and dissolving, each 1/467656th the size of a particle of dust raised by a chariot's wheel in summer.[29] Meditation, like sleep and daydreaming, is associated with reduced activity in certain brain regions. Many psychedelic drugs suppress activity in these same areas (as explored later, in *Neuro-Apocalypse*), and mystics have long exploited them for their trance-inducing properties, whether shamans smoking barks in prehistory or W. B. Yeats and Aleister Crowley mixing mescaline into magick at the end of the nineteenth century. Synthetic drugs entered science with Sir Humphrey Davy at the end of the eighteenth century.[30] His nitrous oxide trips led to a massive philosophical tract on the nature of mind, and he went on to pioneer electrochemistry and discover several elements.

William James's insights with the same drug led to *The Varieties of Religious Experience* (1902),[31] which inaugurated the field of the psychology of religion. Havelock Ellis took mescaline in 1896, describing it as 'not only an unforgettable delight, but an educational influence of no mean value', that was powerful enough to allow him to understand Hegel.[32] He published *Studies in the Psychology of Sex* the following year, introducing the groundbreaking concepts of autoeroticism and narcissism to psychology, and disputing the common assumption that masturbation was pathological in an era when parents deployed clamps and electrified anti-erection devices to protect their children from their beastly urges.[33]

Psychedelics can make people perceive things which are normally obscured. In a demonstration of this in the visual sphere, subjects looking at parallel lines on a screen were asked at what moment the lines become skewed; they were more accurate after a small dose of psilocybin.[34] Straight subjects make a mental note that the lines are parallel, and defer to this model even as the lines begin to diverge. Psychedelics, however, question conceptions and erase the notes we make, so when new information arrives the page is already blank. Dr. Fischer, who conducted the experiment, calls this the 'unlearning… of constancies'.

This capacity, which goes far beyond the visual sphere, made them excellent tools for psychotherapy until they were outlawed. Our constancies may include the assumption that it is the missus who is being unreasonable, not us, or that our addictions are hobbies. But psychedelics question our assumptions. They can also redirect lives. The co-founder of Alcoholics Anonymous lost his compulsion to drink after a spiritual experience with belladonna.[35]

Ayahuasca is, therefore, sometimes described as a mirror held up brutally close to your face, revealing your every blemish. The magnificent iboga root is sometimes described as a waking nightmare; but after crawling through a hell of suppressed memories and mind-loops with a belly full of acrid sawdust, my 13-year daily ganja habit fell away, and my memory and motivation came back, along with vivid technicolour dreams; I emerged from my final bash at drug tourism with the very real possibility that I might finish my book before the end of time. A friend described having his innards torn out and returned to him, bringing an abrupt halt to 26 years of daily alcoholism. *Bassi!* Various drugs, including the notorious ketamine, have proven effective against heroin and alcohol dependence,[36] [37] and in early studies an average of 45% of alcoholics improved with LSD combined with psychotherapy.[38]

Psychologists also self-administered psychoactives, gaining insights into the hidden workings of the human mind, but their findings varied a great deal according to the agent used. Freud's 20-year cocaine habit, for example, might help to explain the form his ground-breaking theory took (the discovery of the ego, deep insights into the nature of neurosis, and a habit of reducing everything that crosses the mind to sex).[39] Harvard psychologist Timothy Leary's pioneering work with psilocybin and then LSD lead him to rather different and increasingly esoteric conceptions of mind.

Acid-emia came into its own in the 1960s, and LSD was another synchronicitous discovery. It was first synthesised in 1938 in Switzerland as one of a series of ergot-based compounds for relief of labour pains, but Albert Hofmann shelved it without noting any special properties. Five years later, due to 'a peculiar presentiment – the feeling that this substance could possess properties other than those established in the first investigations',[40] Hofmann went against lab protocol and remade isotope 25, which soaked through his skin and caused 'unusual sensations' to interrupt his work. Three days later he prepared a cautious dose to test on himself. By today's standards the dose was massive, because LS-serendipi-D was far more potent than anything previously discovered. That afternoon the angel of acid, smirking and with plastic wings, pushed the professor's bicycle down the road towards the psychedelic revolution.[41] The delay was fortunate, as World War II could have been quite different if the fascists on Switzerland's borders had got their hands on LSD before the hippies.

Subjects on LSD score higher in the Purdue Creativity Test, and in tests for originality of word associations[42] and field-dependency[43] (discussed in *Neuro-Apocalypse*). LSD is also a magnificent aid to visualisation. An LSD-enhanced Dr. Kary Mullis visualised the basic molecular concepts of the polymerase chain reaction underpinning DNA testing,[44] and won a Nobel Prize for his efforts. Rumours that Francis Crick glimpsed the double helix structure of DNA on LSD can be neither confirmed nor denied,[45] but the father of molecular genetics was definitely interested in it; he was a founding member of SOMA, a society formed 'to examine without prejudice the scientific, medical, legal, moral, social, and philosophical aspects of heightened mental awareness, with special reference to the effects of pleasure-giving drugs'.[46] It was named SOMA after the wondrous elixir from the Hindu *Vedas*.

LSD 'no sooner eliminates the supremacy of categories than it tears away the ground of its indifference and disintegrates the gloomy dumbshow of stupidity', wrote Michel Foucault.[47] Behind the dumbshow and behind the categories, a deeper level of order may be perceived; and Foucault's own scholarship reveals such a world, describing the historical forces hidden beneath the surface of society. It can also open up entirely new worlds; LSD revealed in 'a moment of clarity' the potentials of cyberspace and the fundamental protocols of virtual reality to its inventor Mark Pesce.[48]

Psychedelics opened Fritjof Capra's eyes to parallels between academic cosmology and Eastern mysticism,[49] as described in his book *The Tao of Physics*. Even the humble ganja plant can be extremely revealing: according to Oxford professor Susan Blackmore, whose research concerns the memes behind the scenes and the genes:

> I can honestly say that without cannabis, most of my scientific research would never have been done and most of my books on psychology and evolution would not have been written.[50]

Paul Erdös, who published more mathematical papers than almost anyone in history, made a similar remark regarding speed. After winning a bet set by a concerned friend to give it a break for a month, he commented simply: 'I'd have no ideas, just like an ordinary person. You've set mathematics back a month.'[51]

Sam Patterson, named 1996 Inventor of the Year by the US Patent Office, is far more chilled. He sits smoking ganja on the beach and doodling cogs until:

> In a brief flash a complete solution goes off. That's when I start sketching like mad. If I'm lucky I can draw it out in the sketch. I don't fully comprehend it until I'm finished.[52]

Many artists meet their muse mashed. Keith Haring's art was cooked in acid. Robert Louis Stevenson wrote *Dr. Jekyll and Mr. Hyde* during six days and nights of a cocaine binge, which explains the story somewhat; he claimed that his tales came from 'the little people who manage man's internal theatre'.[53] Jack Kerouac speeded and sped through pages taped together for hours without pause.[54] Ken Kesey's *One Flew Over the Cuckoo's Nest* was written on acid and mescaline. Ironically, he was switched on when the CIA fed him LSD,[55] and he liked it so much that he administered it all over California. Even England's most esteemed bard was at it. Forensic tests on pipe fragments from Shakespeare's home gave positive results for not only camphor and the hallucinogenic nutmeg, but also for cannabis residues.[56] Maybe he was using more than just metaphor in Sonnet 76:

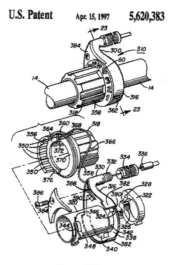

U.S. Patent   Apr. 15, 1997   **5,620,383**

One of Sam
Patterson's patents

Why with the time do I not glance aside

To new-found methods and to compounds strange?

Why write I still all one, ever the same,

And keep invention in a noted weed.

Baudelaire and Victor Hugo also used cannabis for inspiration,[57] but Swinburne and Browning preferred opium. Samuel Coleridge remembered some of the most celebrated lines in English poetry from an opium dream. Curiously, the palace described in the poem is recorded as also having been inspired by a vision, seen in a dream by the original Kubla Khan. Coleridge didn't know about this; his poem was published before the Persian history relating this story was translated.[58]

Ω

As chains of logic relax and trains of thought slow down, insights from the deep mind rise to the surface. Revelatory apocalypses are not at all uncommon in science, and revelation was once part and parcel of scientific endeavour. Johannes Kepler's search for geometric forms in astronomy began with a divine revelation;[59] Paracelsus believed he was 'chosen by God to blot out all the phantasies of elaborate and false works',[60] and that his inspiration came from the astral plane. He certainly wrote like a man possessed, according to a contemporary; constantly and single-mindedly until 'with boots and spurs and fully dressed, he throws himself into bed and rests merely for three hours or so, then writes on again'.[61] This belligerent mishmash of contradictions wandered Europe in a cloud of controversy, baiting gentlemen doctors whilst curing the patients they could not. Town records attest that he cured, for example, over half of the lepers quarantined outside Nuremberg.[62]

Paracelsus was among the first critics of classical humoral theory, and definitely the most energetic. He was also the earliest proponent of the ontological concept of disease – the idea that a disease is a distinct thing in its own right, rather than an imbalance. He cured by tuning in to the specific essence, or 'signature', of the disease, and selecting from nature the plant or mineral with that signature. According to him, the proper goal of alchemy was not making gold but finding specific medicines for specific diseases,[63] and his Great Work developed into modern pharmacology. From his alchemical perspective, he understood the body as a vehicle for transformation, and was the first to describe digestion as a process of separation.

Newton was also an alchemist, and a tenth of his library was devoted to the art.[64] It was meditation on alchemy, not experiment or rational deduction, that brought him to the theory of gravity; and it happened during the period of his life dedicated most completely to alchemical experiments.[65] He took the maxim *As above, so below* from *The Emerald Tablet of Hermes Trismegistus*, and applied it to the motion of bodies in both the microcosm and the macrocosm. Before Newton, physics was a fragmentary set of theories applied to different situations. Gravity, however, was the first universal theory in intellectual history governing different scales, both apples falling and planets orbiting. It was also alchemical thinking which revealed to him that:

> The changing of bodies into light, and light into bodies,
> is very conformable to the course of Nature, which
> seems delighted with transmutations.[66]

His intuition has since been confirmed in the particle accelerator, but at the time transmutation was the exclusive domain of priests, transforming wine into the blood of Christ. Alchemy was illegal, and he only avoided trouble by maintaining what he called a 'high silence' regarding the art.[67]

The apocalyptic mind sees the bigger picture. Where his contemporaries focused on men's agency in the world, Paracelsus perceived that both men and women have an equal part in conception; he was also one of first to write about, indeed to care about, women's diseases.[68] His study of miner's sickness was the first to recognise a disease caused by pollution, appreciating the reciprocity between man and environment.[69] Paracelsus brought together alchemy, natural philosophy and medicine for the first time. Similarly Newton married maths, mechanics and astronomy, and Swedenborg united practically every branch of the Tree of Knowledge into his hierarchy of forms. This process of integration is another apocalypse, where the veils separating distinct disciplines fall.

Scientists like Paracelsus and Newton can be thought of as apocalyptic in another sense, as their ideas extended society's collective horizons, overturning common conceptions about the cosmos, or order of things (*kosmos* in Greek). But many of these men were also apocalyptic in the more vulgar sense. Among his many eccentricities, Paracelsus was a screaming apocalyptic, preaching drunken doom in the tavern whenever the spirit took him. For him, the end was damn well nigh, as he wrote in his *Prophecy for the next Twenty-four Years*;[70] but he died in 1541, before his prophecies had time to mature. His predictions concerning floods, the Antichrist and New Jerusalem are considered an unfortunate annex to his more serious work laying the foundations of modern medicine. Swedenborg's apocalypticism was more sober, though no less fervent. He believed that God had chosen him to announce the coming of the New Church, which followed the Last Judgment of 1757.[71]

Newton is remembered as an arch-rationalist, who whipped the Royal Society into shape by restricting scientific endeavour to observation and mathematical modelling (rather than trying to generate frogs from mud, for example). But the primary obsession of this very obsessive man was the end of the world. *Isaacus Neuutonus* saw his mission in the anagram of his Latinized name, *Ieova sanctus unus*,[72] and believed that he was chosen by Jehovah to interpret *The Book of Daniel*. His massive, ultimately incomplete project to calculate the end of days dwarfed his conventional projects, taking over 50 years and running to 4500 pages. His interest in astronomy and chronology was secondary to this, stemming from his desire to date events in scripture and decipher omens in the sky.

In times past, mystics, magicians and empirics were allies struggling against the constraints of religion. While priests explained from the pulpit what long dead people had thought about the universe, others were grabbing reality by the nuts to see what happens when you fiddle with it. United by curiosity, which St. Augustine called 'lust of the eyes',[73] magicians and proto-scientists manipulated rare materials and obscure symbols, tested predictions about the future, and produced potent agents. Things changed as the shadow of the Enlightenment fell over Europe. Spirits were banished from the lab, and eventually even God was ousted. Philosophy continued to fall until it hit the ground with reductivist materialism. Science became the daddy, religion shrivelled into a doddery granddad wheeled out for special occasions, and mysticism became a mad aunt, humoured and derided by turns, and liable to make right-thinking people uncomfortable. But loonies occasionally come out with something extremely perceptive.

One might be tempted to think that Newton and Swedenborg were the last scientist-mystics, but Schrödinger found in Vedanta answers to quantum questions,[74] and *The Upanishads* pointed Bohr towards his revolutionary conception of reality.[75] Alfred Wallace, the malarial Darwinist, wrote a book called *On Miracles and Modern Spiritualism.*[76] This field was popular with many nineteenth-century scientists: Nobel laureate Lord Rayleigh,[77] who discovered argon and much besides; Augustus De Morgan,[78] who expanded Boolean algebra and undertook the earliest scientific investigations of séances; Sir William Crookes, who discovered cathode rays and performed some of the pinoeering work in plasma chemistry and radioactivity. Crookes was nearly kicked out of the Royal Society for his report on four years of experiments at his lab, which included levitation, the spontaneous appearance of writing and luminous bodies.[79] The superstar Spiritist scientist, however, was Marie Curie, who also treated the séance as science, employing controls and taking detailed notes.[80] She became the first female Nobel laureate with her demonstration of radioactivity, and is one of only four scientists in history to win two Nobel prizes.

Both sides of the apocalyptic mind continued to surface in the highest echelons of twentieth and twenty-first century science. Einstein's doomy side can be seen in his comment that 'it appears glaringly that civilised mankind finds itself at present in grave danger',[81] and his prediction that 'World War IV will be fought with sticks and stones'.[82] This was in response to nuclear weapons technology, made possible by his monumental discovery, expressed mathematically as $E=mc^2$ and militarily as the atom bomb. Richard Feynman and Julius Oppenheimer were also instrumental in the production of the A-bomb, and all three physicists were deeply concerned that it might exterminate humanity. Oppenheimer directed the Los Alamos laboratory, but turned against the programme and died convinced that it meant the end of humanity.

The doomy tradition in physics continues with Stephen Hawking, who occupies the chair that Newton once held at Cambridge. After having reconceptualised our universe as a boundless entity with hidden dimensions, and going some way to answer questions about our beginnings, he posed a question about our end:

In a world that is in chaos politically, socially and environmentally, how can the human race sustain another 100 years?[83]

'I don't know', came his answer a month later.[84] Who knows? The answers to big questions lie beyond the range of normal perception, and come to us via mysterious pathways, in trances, dreams, or in sudden insights brought on by drugs or disease. The mystical revelations and flashes of inspiration of men such as Tycho, Bruno, Boyle, Pascal, Copernicus, Newton, Kepler and Einstein have illuminated the world with understanding, and brought fabulous inventions into our lives. They may have also brought us closer to our doom.

Both sides of the apocalyptic mind come together in a quote by Einstein:

A new type of thinking is essential if mankind is to survive and move towards higher levels.[85]

An apocalypse begins with one person, and is not uncommon; but personal apocalypses can accumulate, and tear through the veil on a collective level. Apocalypses at both the personal and collective scales are examined in delicious detail in the next two books of the series, but for now let us stay with revelation in science, and focus on some of the controversies that have attended new ideas. We will see that when intellectual breakthroughs begin to threaten models in which much is invested, scientific institutions can employ deeply unscientific means to maintain a monopoly on the interpretation of reality.

4. THE POLITICS OF TRUTH

To the Marquis Sabnock

> Man's mind, once stretched by a new idea, never regains its original dimensions.[1]

Oliver Wendal Holmes Sr.

The usually cheery Spaniard looked pitifully at his twisted ankle, and asked if anyone could get him some anti-inflammatories from town. We were in a clearing in the Amazon, so I pointed out a *pião roxo* plant a few feet away. He was sceptical, but he was also desperate, because he could barely walk and no one was driving, so he mournfully rubbed the leaves into his leg. Within the hour he was back to his cheery, uninflamed self, and perhaps a little wiser.

I found no handy herb on the streets of La Paz when my girlfriend showed me a weird blistery thing that had appeared on her cheek. The pharmacist explained that this fungus could be treated with pills today or injections tomorrow, by which time it would have overtaken her face. I said it was her face and her choice, but I wouldn't eat his pills, and neither would

I have eaten that skanky-looking chicken the night before. We calmly watched the blisters arise and pass, migrating around her face and neck for the next few hours, and that was that; she was absolutely fine, with no more lasting effects than a healthy aversion to greasy skewered filth.

It is wise to think critically about what we consume. For good evolutionary reasons we are wary of the unfamiliar and comfortable with the known, which means we sometimes reject ideas that are difficult to digest. Let us be sceptical of all ideas and all sources, whether orthodox or fringe, new or old, familiar or strange, as we examine the evidence below – gathered from research institutions as sound as any in the field of science, with citations for further reading. This chapter might be something of a cardboard soufflé to chew through, but some detail is required to shed light on the machinery of knowledge production.

The father of the scientific method was Francis Bacon, who formalised the process of induction to exclude the four 'idols' that obscure our clear apprehension of the truth.[2] These are (1) the human tendency to exaggerate, which is compounded by (2) individual prejudices, (3) attachment to philosophies, and (4) distortions caused by use of language. Inductivism begins with observations made under a wide range of conditions. Data are tabulated, patterns sought, and finally general laws governing the patterns are worked out (induced). We observe, for example, the sun in the east every morning, under different conditions: in cloudy and clear skies; in London and Virginia. A pattern emerges, and a law is induced: the sun rises in the east. This is the scientific method, in theory. In practice, however, a great deal of prejudice passes through the pipette.

In the nineteenth century, Oliver Wendell Holmes Sr. collected case studies on puerperal fever, which killed about one in five mothers shortly after childbirth. He noticed a pattern: the fever nearly always struck a woman tended by a doctor who had just finished doing one of two things – performing an autopsy on a victim, or assisting labour for a woman who would later fall sick. He proposed that the disease was iatrogenic, meaning that it was caused by medical intervention, and that the vector was the administering doctor himself.[3]

Not only was Holmes suggesting that the Hippocratic oath 'to do no harm' was being violated, he was also denying contemporary medical theory, which did not recognise infection. He could not imagine the mechanism of disease transfer; he simply begged his colleagues to wash their hands between deliveries. Baconian inductivism generates laws governing patterns, and excludes thoretical concerns from the process of knowledge creation. It does not need theories to explain the laws revealed, but Holmes's colleagues did. The idea of action at a distance reeked of magic, and offended the sensibilities of the enlightenment gentlemen. His discovery was ignored, his evidence brushed aside, and his hygienic measures rejected as foolish superstition.

Five years later, hospital manager Ignaz Semmelweis had the same revelation, and introduced simple hygienic procedures to his hospitals.[4] Despite practically eliminating puerperal fever, he was dismissed from his posts, publicly ridiculed, and hounded by the Viennese medical establishment. Driven to the madhouse by the needless deaths and orphaned babies, he was eventually beaten to death by asylum orderlies – just as Pasteur's new germ theory began spreading through Europe, and medics finally started washing their hands. Doctors today claim Semmelweis and Holmes as martyrs in the battle against superstition, but is medicine any more open to new ideas? A tale from the 1980s suggests otherwise.

Dr. Jacques Benveniste, research director for the French National Institute for Health (INSERM), was initially sceptical when commissioned to test homoeopathic dilutions, which are prepared by diluting a drug repeatedly up to 30 times sequentially. Avogadro's number predicts that the twelfth dilution retains only about one molecule of the drug; beyond that, according to the theory, the samples are just water.

The prestigious immunologist was selected because he had developed a widely used assay, in which white blood cells are introduced to an agent, then stained with dye. Healthier cells absorb more dye, so they are more likely to be spotted under a microscope by a lab technician. The number counted in a sample gives an indication of the average health of the cells, and therefore the potency of the agent.

Measurements of homeopathic dilutions taken in this way indicated a decline in potency, as expected – until the tenth sample. But then, the potency rose again. Benveniste was surprised to record that it fell, rose, fell again, rose and so on; in a periodic wave.[5] In 250 further experiments over two and a half years, Benveniste's team consistently measured the pharmacological effect of pure water, and in 1988 he submitted his findings to the prestigious scientific journal *Nature*. At this point, the machinations of the scientific establishment become interesting.

The editor of *Nature*, John Maddox, demanded replications. The Baconian method does indeed require that results be replicable, meaning that a repeat experiment produces similar results; but academia does not usually ask for replications *before* publication. The peer review process is a *re*view, where critique follows *after* publication. Benveniste acquiesced all the same, and sent his methodology to French, Italian, Canadian and Israeli labs. After four successful replications, *Nature* printed his paper, along with an incredulous editorial.[6]

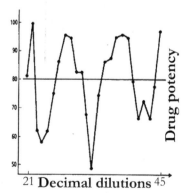

21 **Decimal dilutions** 45

The following issue contained many letters disputing his findings, including one alleging fraud, by suggesting that the figures were too good to be true. Benveniste's response, pointing out the critic's error in neglecting to square a value, was never printed.[7] Maddox did, however, promise to publish further research conducted as a blind trial. The blind trial yielded a positive result, but Maddox reneged on his promise, citing statistical inconsistencies – this despite the fact that the paper was co-signed by a professor of statistics.[8]

Maddox next demanded to oversee an experiment, taking to the lab not biologists but stage magician and TV sceptic James 'The Incredible' Randi. Lab technicians were made to conduct experiments at twice their normal pace while the fraud squad harassed and shouted at them, and the Incredible, incredulous Randi performed disruptive magic tricks as they counted cells. The visitors also insisted on doing the pipetting, despite being laypeople with no experience of this delicate procedure. *Nature* published three negative results, and judged Benveniste to be fraudulent. Benveniste's reply – claiming that three positive results were not reported, that one negative was in fact neutral, and that two others were due to poor pipetting – was not printed.

Another sceptic tested her suspicions more appropriately, coordinating double-blind experiments in four independent labs. The replications were all successful, and she commented that 'the results compel me to suspend my disbelief and to start searching for rational explanations.'[9] Over the next six years, at least 21 successful replications were made in other labs.[10] *Nature* ignored them all, reporting only a failure in 1993.

Denying replication is a standard tactic of the scientific reactionary. Newton's opponents argued for 50 years that his experiments in splitting light with a prism could not be repeated, although schoolchildren manage it today. Another standard tactic is to ignore data and attack theory. 'There is no objective explanation for these observations,' complained

Maddox's editorial;[11] but this is science upside down, wind from the professor's bottom. Inductivism begins not with theory but with observation; because, as Bacon noted, 'what a man would like to be true, he preferentially believes'.[12] This may be an entirely unconscious process, which makes it doubly pernicious. Presumably the pharmaceuticals companies advertising in the pages of *Nature* might have preferentially disbelieved in remedies composed of nothing but water.

Benveniste began experimenting with a macabre device called a Langendorff apparatus, which measures the rate of the still-beating heart from a freshly killed guinea pig as a drug solution passes through it. Again, homoeopathic dilutions were measured to alter a physiological process. Benveniste also learned that heating the water or subjecting it to a strong magnetic field disrupted the effect. He began to investigate an electromagnetic (EM) mechanism for the memory of water, using a transmission machine, and found that running an electric current between a drug solution and a vessel of pure water also produced a sample that slowed the heart. This EM signature tested as pharmacologically active when recorded and e-mailed double-blind to another lab.[13]

Italian physicists specialising in coherent domain theory were invited to investigate further, but Benveniste's employer INSERM vetoed the visit, and also attempted to censor his research. He was also put on probation following a lab visit where his experimental practices were found to be exemplary, but his publication of the unorthodox findings was judged as a misuse of scientific authority.[14]

Benveniste was ruffling feathers all over the shop. His lab and another found that the supposedly pure physiological serum distributed by the Paris medical service caused immunised hearts to stop beating. He suggested that EM contamination made it act as a toxin, and that it might be an iatrogenic contributor to cot death in hypersensitive babies who had recently been vaccinated. When Benveniste began inviting audiences to public double-blind experiments, INSERM sent him a threatening letter:

> I very seriously draw your attention to the pernicious character of the spreading of such 'information'. Should you persist in this type of behaviour, I would be forced to draw serious consequences from it.[15]

Benveniste went ahead with the impudence of a French revolutionary, and his funding was cut. Despite being one of the top immunologists in the country, the scientific press has published nothing more of his work since. He died in 2004.

Ω

Homeopathy was born into controversy, in an era before 'orthodox medicine' existed. Practitioners cured and competed in the medical marketplace, including bonesetters, herbalists, apothecaries, barber-surgeons and exorcists, each with their own theories and techniques. The wealthy favoured gentlemen physicians, who tended to them without touching them, sometimes without even seeing them. The system employed was allopathic, restoring balance by working against (*allo*) symptoms presented by the disease (*pathy*). A fever, therefore, might be countered by spilling overheated blood until the patient passed out. Syphilis was tackled with a 'heroic dose' of mercury, which cost an arm and a leg – and even the teeth, which often fell out from heavy metal poisoning. A disillusioned Dr. Hahnemann gave up his sickening profession to become a translator, and came upon the principle of treating 'like with like' when translating the Hippocratic corpus. Intrigued, he tested a traditional malaria remedy on himself, and found it produced the fever and shakes associated with malaria.

Homoeopathic medicines cause the same (*homo*) symptoms (*pathy*) as the disease, and are given at high dilutions. The modality quickly became popular amongst patients, with some spectacular results. In the 1854 cholera epidemic, less than

17% of patients at the Golden Square Homoeopathic Hospital perished, compared to over half in other London hospitals.[16] These impressive data were initially suppressed, but came to light when a sympathetic aristocrat began asking questions in the House of Lords. An allopathic reaction began in earnest. Medical students were expelled for studying the heresy, practitioners were blackballed from medical societies. Journals began rejecting papers on homoeopathy outright, as they continue to do today.

Prejudice was enshrined in law with the 1858 Medical Health Act, separating allopaths from their competitors, including herbalists, homoeopaths, bone-setters, wise women, mesmerists, midwives, and others. The medical marketplace was polarised along class lines, between orthodox and quack factions. Doctors and new graduates joined a new medical register, and could be struck off the list for referring a patient to a herbalist. Doctoring became what it is today: a set of techniques practised by a closed group, almost exclusively schooled in allopathic theory.

Benveniste's forays across the lines, and the blood cells and beating hearts he brought back, raise questions. With research suspended, most of the answers will remain beyond the pale and beyond the veil for the time being. But while the effects of high dilutions on our bodies are unclear, the effects on the marketplace are easily measured – especially in France, where a quarter of prescriptions are already homoeopathic.

Scientific controversies trace the line between orthodox theories and theories of a 'pernicious character', and the disputes surrounding Benveniste, Hahnemann, Holmes and Semmelweis present patterns to the inductivist seeking them. Firstly, theory is put before observation, and anomalous data is excluded. Secondly, supposedly 'scientific' institutions settle disputes by unscientific means, including censorship, ridicule, intimidation, allegations of fraud, obstructing research and cutting funding. Thirdly, the medical establishment reacts particularly vigorously to issues of iatrogenic illness, where medical practice itself is implicated.

Discovery happens when the veil falls for an individual, revealing a deeper level of reality. This may happen through insight or hypnagogic trance, or when a scientist suspends their disbelief long enough to apply the scientific method, and integrate the results into their cosmology. When a discovery is integrated into wider society, as with Copernicus's heliocentric system or Kekulé's structural theory, then a personal apocalypse becomes a collective resource, opening up new fields of inquiry and experience. As we will see in *Apocalypses Past, Present and Personal*, a rush of insights can sometimes precipitate an acute period of wide-ranging social and philosophical upheavals.

There is nothing so disruptive to the status quo as a radical new idea, and perhaps this is why the border between the personal and collective apocalypse is particularly tightly patrolled when the ideas are potentially groundbreaking.

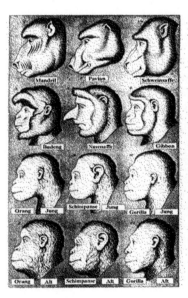 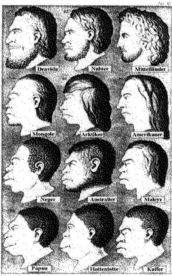

Our system of knowledge production is not science but Scientism, an updated version of the one 'true' truth. Science raises questions, but Scientism shuts down avenues of inquiry and maintains the status quo, as did former state philosophies. Whereas medieval women were oppressed, publicly humiliated and sometimes executed, as befitted creatures susceptible to  the serpent's cunning, the Enlightenment laid such superstition to rest. The true source of female irrationality was revealed to be the womb (*hysterium* in Greek, hence 'hysteria'), and later authorities disqualified women from voting and other intellectual tasks on account of their smaller brains. Likewise, Catholic slavers justified their trade by reference to Noah's curse on the descendants of Ham, whom they assumed to be black; Humanist slave-traders, however, cited 'scientific' racial theories. During the feudal age, the English class system was brutally maintained as a faithful reflection of the hierarchy of Heaven, and in the age of eugenics it was considered a natural and desirable result of Darwinian forces. It was not science but rioting that challenged this bigotry, fired up by Emmeline Pankhurst, Malcolm X, and other political radicals. Even so, wage slavery and class divisions persist, and are considered to be a natural and desirable outcome of a free and fair economic system, the one true truth to which There Is No Alternative. For the time being.

Another troublesome spectre Benveniste invoked was electromagnetism – a phenomenon which had haunted the academy since the late eighteenth century, when Dr. Franz Mesmer described 'animal magnetism' surrounding and connecting living bodies. His prancing around perfumed rooms in Paris manipulating this force and throwing women into fits prompted his former patron Louis XVI to call an investigation. The cogs turned then just as they do now: case studies of beneficial results were ignored, and investigators focused on theory. They could not measure this invisible field, and concluded that it was complete humbug, while releasing a secret report describing Mesmerism as a threat to public morality. Mesmer was 'exposed' by a fraud squad and fled Paris in disgrace. Medics dabbling in the field lost their practices. Curious medical students risked expulsion.

Despite this, Mesmerism flirted with respectability the following century, beginning with Professor John Elliotson, physician to University College Hospital and pioneer of the stethoscope. He presented an account of an amputation under mesmeric trance to the Royal Medical and Chirurgical Society, of which he had once been president.[17] The assembled gentlemen concluded that he was either mistaken, or that the patient had been trained not to react as a saw passed through his bone.[18] Undeterred, Elliotson began to perform mesmeric surgery himself,[19] earning furious attacks in the medical press and the loss of his academic posts. His student Dr. James Esdaile went on to oversee over a thousand mesmeric operations at his Calcutta hospital,[20] and the medical community concluded that the weak-minded Hindus had been tricked into not flinching when an arm, cataract or penis was removed. Dr. Clocquet's comparable researches in France were explained away in a similar manner.[21]

Again, the whiff of iatrogenic disease offended orthodox noses. Nineteenth-century surgeons subdued patients with strong drink and strong men, and nearly half of the amputees died, compared to only 5% of Esdaile's. When ether anaesthesia was discovered later in the decade, it was welcomed as a weapon, not against pain so much as against mesmerism. Easily administered by any fool with a handkerchief, it successfully kept sorcerers out of the theatre.[22] Though anaesthetics

have come a long way since toxic substances like ether and chloroform, they still kill people,[23] whereas no one has ever been hypnotised to death. Although mesmeric surgery and dentistry occasionally appear in the popular press, the medical press will not report on this promising technique – testament to the skilful political machinations of physicians of the mid-1800s.

Wilhelm Reich's cancer treatments in the 1950s also involved invisible waves, or 'orgone'. Though he was never prosecuted, his books were burned, his equipment was destroyed, and he died in a police cell, not unlike Semmelweis a century before. More recently Yves Rocard, father of the French atom and hydrogen bombs, head of physics at the École Normale Supérieure, as well as a war hero and the father of a prime minister, lost his research grant. His *faux pas* was to claim to have measured, with the help of water diviners, the EM field of water.

Ω

How powerful is industrial medicine without *Realpolitik* to support it? A top US Department of Health official estimates that 80% of the funds his office channels have no effect on improving health, and that much of the remainder deals with iatrogenic illness.[24] Over 100,000 Americans die each year from drugs *correctly* administered by hospital staff, and over two million more suffer from serious side effects.[25]

By the time the first antibiotics were manufactured in 1945, epidemics were already becoming rarer and less severe. Life expectancy was rising and infant mortality was falling, due to improved hygiene, nutrition, sewerage and housing.[26] Deaths from tuberculosis, scarlet fever, measles, diphtheria and whooping cough had fallen by around 90% before immunisation programs began; and while mortality rates of some diseases declined briefly, sleeping sickness, malaria and leishmaniasis returned with a vengeance within a generation. Other victories may be similarly short-lived.

My granny was a tailor from the Transylvanian *shtetl*, and way too paranoid to let a doctor anywhere near her. She never took anything more potent than garlic, and I never saw her with even a cold or a headache. When she died, at the age of 86, she had a full head of black hair, all her teeth and all her peculiar marbles. At age 14, I tested the theory that your scalp produces oils to wash your hair if you give up shampoo. After the first eight weeks of itch and stink, the hypothesis was upheld, and decades of soap-dodging later my hair today is fragrant and dashing. At 15 I rejected brainwashing along with hair-washing, and gave up all chemicals except the strictly recreational. My occasional colds and fevers pass quickly, and ganja and meditation in combination make for a good painkiller. The unhappy Dr. Holmes exhorted his peers to cast into the sea the entire *materia medica*, except opium, wine, and 'a few specifics which our doctor's art did not discover'.[27] Sadly, opium is defined as class A today (that is, having no medical application); in the absence of a good contact, I begrudgingly resorted to ibuprofen twice in the last 20 years.

My one serious illness began in the Amazon with a bite from a sand fly, which rapidly grew into a two-inch ulcer streaming eerie coloured fluids. Leishmaniasis is an aggressive and potentially fatal bacterial parasite; every doctor, medical authority, and alternative therapist I asked insisted that it would not yield to natural medicines. The second phase could dissolve the cartilage in my nose, my throat and my joints, I was told. On being offered a series of 180 intravenous shots or more of antimony potassium tartrate, I followed two simple rules from *The Gospel of Thomas*: don't lie, and don't do what you hate.[28] I hate the idea of heavy metals in my organs, and I can't stand injections – not the pain so much as handing authority over my body to a doctor. Regarding being truthful, I was editing this lovely little book at the time, and couldn't honestly continue if I was medicating with jabs.

I attacked my foe with diets and teas, with buckets of lemons and heroic doses of ayahuasca, which is what I had gone to the Amazon to learn about in the first place. Here was my opportunity to see just how potent a medicine it was, with a daily dose at 4am for many months of my cure. My days circled around the wound, constantly cleaning it, shielding it, thinking about it. Locals hassled me endlessly to take injections, because the spell of Scientism has fallen even over the largest natural pharmacy on the planet. *'Têm que se humilhar'*, they said; but I didn't want to be humble, not to a bacteria, and not to their pharma-fetishes and adopted witch doctors.

My boil shrank and swelled over eight months as I battled microbes and unruly spirits. But in fearing that I might lose my nose, I discovered what a gift a healthy nose is, what a joy a body is. My flesh rotted, worms hatched in my ulcer; it took away ten kilos and one ex-wife (who had come back into my life as the nurse from hell). It also rent the veil by smashing my rose-tinted spectacles, and left me not just better but rebooted, ready to face the world on my own terms.

Traditional medicine is intelligent, with complex and responsive interactions between plant and pathogen, patient and practitioner. Ginseng works differently with different conditions, promoting blood vessel growth in wounds but inhibiting blood vessel growth in tumours.[29] Whereas isolated pharmacological agents strike at limited, specific sites, turmeric is active in at least 60 molecular processes involved in cancer treatment, protecting healthy cells, inhibiting tumour growth and metastasis, reducing inflammation, scarring and so on.[30] It is, however, poorly absorbed into the body, unless in the presence of black pepper.[31] Indian mothers were grinding up this wisdom into curry paste for millennia before biochemists discovered it and began theorising about it.

Plant compounds work together in complex synergy. Acetylsalicylic acid, isolated from white willow bark or meadowsweet and marketed as aspirin, is a good analgesic, but it causes gastrointestinal bleeding and ulcers. A study of hospital admissions for adverse drug reactions implicated low-dose aspirin in 18% of admissions, and found it responsible for 61% of the resulting deaths.[32]

Both meadowsweet and white willow bark, however, contain other compounds that protect the alimentary canal from the acid. Weight-loss pills containing ephedrine (refined from ephedra) work faster than tea made with the plant's leaves; but the synthetic compound has been implicated in tragic fatalities, because it also raises blood pressure.[33] Ephedra, however, contains compounds that counteract this property.

Amazonian Indians harvest a secretion from the glands of a frog on the full moon, and carefully return the frog to its branch afterwards. This *kambo* contains many known anaesthetic, tranquilliser, antibiotic, and antifungal compounds; but whatever it did to push the ligaments of my friend's knee back into alignment after a motorbike accident involves something else. Indians also use it to halt a string of bad luck, and to sharpen the eyes for a hunt. Pharmacology is not yet equipped to appreciate the magnificent complexity of these medicines, the intricate interactions between compounds, species, kingdoms and habitats. Soothing dock leaves grow next to stinging nettles, coca relieves altitude sickness in its native Andean highlands, and anti-febrile cinchona grows in malaria-infested jungles. Something far cleverer than your doctor is orchestrating this symphony, but if you don't trust the wisdom of the planet, what do you trust? Big Pharma?

While pharmacies appear to sell the fruits of scientific research, maybe they simply capitalise on ignorance. Many ailments both trivial and serious yield to herbs that can be grown in window boxes, and antibiotics and tonics grow wild on the moors; but the witches and the wildernesses are dying out, and we prefer doctor's orders to Granny's specifics. Laws passed since the Medical Health Act continue to diminish our autonomy. Since the *neem* plant was patented in 1985, traditional healers in India must break the law to use it in their own preparations.[34]

Good doctors are restricted by their training, and bad ones are given license to fiddle physiology, strip veins and cut you open, without necessarily addressing imbalances. Disease is more than a set of symptoms: it is a call to attention, and an opportunity to learn. In my mid-20s, a spot of eczema sometimes greeted me the morning after a night on the piss. A Japanese doctor I taught gave me some steroid cream, which I accepted out of politeness but ditched as soon as I left the building. Eczema was my friend, tapping me on the hand to encourage a well-needed change of lifestyle, and maybe averting liver damage or worse down the line.

Allopathic medicine works against symptoms, and against the wisdom of the body. In all but the most extreme instances, however, the body knows what it is doing, which is why Zulus traditionally responded to signs of fever by wrapping up in blankets under the sun, treating like with like. A fever running its normal course confines you to your bed, to rest and sweat out toxins. Higher temperatures favour the enzymes of your immune system, while slowing down invading pathogens. Painkillers mercifully take away serious pain. Listen to the message of a twisted ankle at full volume, though, and you might avoid stressing it as it heals, and take more care on the stairs in the future.

Tablets don't rectify a poor diet or sleep regimen, which impacts upon many bodily and cognitive processes. Zoloft and Prozac help you grin and bear an abusive relationship or dead-end job; but misery and frustration might push you to quit, or to tell your boss what you think of her. You might even smash the state! But most of us are walking cocktails, regularly imbibing antibiotics, both directly and indirectly via factory-farmed meat. Our diminished and confused immune systems are turning upon their hosts, with soaring rates of asthma, hay fever, AIDS, ME, rheumatoid arthritis and other autoimmune syndromes.

We also have new interventions for new diseases. Whereas people used to get 'anxious', now we suffer from 'anxiety', or even 'GAD' (generalised anxiety disorder). From adjective to noun to acronym, the disorder emerges until it exists independently of the anxious person, becoming far more virulent, and easier to monetise. Tranquilliser use is increasing six times faster than illegal opiate abuse, and twelve times faster than alcoholism. Prescriptions for insomnia have doubled since 2001.[35] Disrupted sleep is one of the first hints that something is out of balance, and with all-night TV advertising sleeping pills and all-night pharmacies selling them, the chief medical advisor for the US Consumers Union noted astutely that pharmaceuticals companies 'helped create the disease.'[36]

Syndromes and many other new diseases are rarely discovered; they are invented. Obesity was never a disease, it was too many pies. Childbirth has become increasingly medicalised; 30% of births in the US are by Caesarean section, representing an increase of nearly 50% in a decade.[37] Big noses did not require surgery until recently, but despite Americans spending over twelve billion dollars per year on cosmetic operations,[38] women with breast implants are still three times more likely to commit suicide than their untreated peers.[39] Like much of modern medicine, fake tits are superficially impressive, but leave much to be desired on closer inspection. The *Cosmo* beauty myth hides an ugly secret. When young men re-sculpt their jawlines, or grandmothers staple their faces into expressions of permanent youthful surprise, are they being treated for physical disorders or exploited for psychological ones?

Editors of nature (such as the editor of *Nature*) have long presumed to dictate what right-thinking folk think about; but I think something smells fishy. And judging by the extreme reactions, the fishiest fish swim in EM waves. The link between microwave radiation and cancer was first established in 1973,[40] a year before the personal computer went on the market; but this revelation has yet to leave the priestly enclaves of science and penetrate into public consciousness. Back when it was first discovered that microwaves heat things up, safety guidelines were set at an arbitrary 10% of the level required to warm meat, but much lower levels disrupt *in vitro* cell signalling and cell division.[41] Today, we are exposed to 100–200 million times natural radiation levels, and malignant cancers have doubled in a generation.[42] Surveys of the populations of entire nations link power lines and mobile phones to cancer, to Alzheimer's and diabetes, and the WHO recognises conditions where everyday radiation levels cause headaches, tinnitus and cognitive dysfunction. Studies funded by the Electric Power Institute found no link to cancer, as might be expected. Otherwise, the evidence is overwhelming.

But Scientism, as a belief system at the personal level, is not especially evidence-based. When a science teacher explains that prayer doesn't affect anything, or that your prayers might help cure your disease but won't influence the weather, they are engaging in priestcraft, not science. A scientific approach would involve gathering data, looking for patterns, and testing claims. For my part, when a Brazilian friend cautioned me not to keep my phonecard in my wallet, because my coins would drain it of units, I didn't test the claim. I just rejected it as absurd – but not because of any evidence. I just don't think the cosmos works like that. Why waste my time?

Likewise, the majority of people with fixed opinions on homeopathy have never studied the evidence, may never have read a biomedical journal, and do not uderstand the politics of knowledge production. Our beliefs are usually founded on either the appeal to authority ('Einstein said...'), or the appeal to common sense. And common sense is demarcated, in no small measure, by authorities, both political and scientific.

When something unfamiliar enters our world, we instinctively run back to daddy. It used to be chiefs and prophets, then the Pope took over, and now patriarchs wear lab coats, but robes do not free a scientist from unscientific prejudices, any more than a priest's frock spares him from unchristian lusts. Catholics feared magick despite, or perhaps because, Catholicism is steeped in magical rite, lore and thinking. Superstitious sorts of scientistics fear the unproved and unordered, although nothing is ever proved in science, and order is a matter of perspective.

While administering to our aching bones over the centuries, a priestly class of physicians, pharmacists, psychiatrists and their forbears have struggled for control over our bodies, and over our beliefs concerning them. Children are taught the creed from hallowed textbooks, and sit for confirmation in exam halls. 'The intelligent layman' grows up with reasonable – but ultimately unprovable – dogmas about his world, which come down to him complete, as articles of faith. And the rest be damned.

No religion ever managed to implant such a narrow spectrum of beliefs across such a broad swathe of the world. Now, as in the days of the Holy Roman Empire, the layman is shielded from heresy, and chief amongst the blasphemies are those that reek of magick: Semmelweis's touch of death; action at a distance; invisible fields; charged potions; and the sympathetic principle of treating like with like.

INSERM described Benveniste's experiments as 'black magic',[43] but the real black magicians have reality pinned down with rubber gloves. Black/white, wrong/right, left/right – a hex on both your houses! Reality is far more colourful than that. Over the next few books, we will leave our surgically sculpted and sewn-up bodies of knowledge behind, and look to less sterile zones to make sense of the mystery, reaching a little deeper into the crack between science and magick to see how our fingers smell when they come out.

For now, however, let us pinch our noses and sift through another festering bin full of the Enlightenment project, where laws multiply like flies upon the decaying sinews of the modern state.

Now wash your hands.

5. SHOCKING SUBJECTS: LAW AND DISORDER

To the ruler of the unruly.

A state? What is that? It is a lie!… whatever it sayeth it lieth; and whatever it hath it hath stolen … 'it is I who am the regulating finger of God' – thus roareth the monster … The state, … where the slow suicide of all – is called 'life'. Just see these superfluous ones! They steal the works of the inventors and the treasures of the wise … and everything becometh sickness and trouble unto them! … Sick are they always: they vomit their bile and call it a newspaper. … badly they all smell to me, these idolaters. My brethren, will ye suffocate in the fumes of their maws and appetites! Better break the windows and jump into the open air!'[1]

Friedrich Nietzsche

Plain-clothes coppers swooped the moment my girlfriend passed me a joint. Her pockets were full of all sorts, but they only searched mine, and found a tiny bag of 'vegetable material'. They threw me in a van, where I sat in lotus and invoked Mercury, to take him down the station as my advocate.

Now it so happened, that night in Manchester in 1997, that I had magick sigils painted down my arms; and the officers mocked me, according to their custom: 'You a student, are yer? What'yer studyin', eh? Witchcraft?' They chuckled when they noticed that their first catch of the day was an occultist, on Friday 13th before sunrise, and laughed heartily when I asked if I could hang on to a gnarly-looking talismanic necklace. They bagged it anyway, but when it went into bag number 666 their laughing stopped, and it was *WE* who were smirking mercurial. Mercury, mockery and ecstasy make for a cheeky mix. Our shrunken irises confounded the officer collecting our biometric data. 'Blue-green!' We giggled helpfully. 'Greeny-bluey blue!' We spent our time between manic interviews demanding things and muttering incantations, and by the time our prints were taken, the officer pressing the seal of our diabolical fingers had brought his crucifix out from under his shirt.

The police let me go uncharged; I let them go unhexed. We are all subjects subject to the state, born into an illusion that compromise is freedom, bound by the same borders, lines drawn in blood. The state enforces the boundaries of acceptable behaviour, as Scientism marks out the boundaries of acceptable thought. Both arose in Europe at the close of the medieval period, in conjunction with the first standing armies, which allowed both Scientism and Statism to expand across the globe with the Age of Discovery. As the Early Modern period got underway, knights, priests and peasants serving their king were superseded by soldiers, scientists and citizens serving the state. They were joined by policemen when the first constabulary was formed in 1829.

The state I was born into is a democracy, where in theory the people (*demo*) have the power (*kratis*) to alter the law, through elected representatives. Indeed, the state is finally abandoning laws that persecute queers, while simultaneously writing laws to persecute the poor, quietly institutionalising corporatism while loudly braying about progressive policies. That same democracy persecuted women until a gang of brick-throwing arsonists overthrew what was considered to be the natural order, succeeding where 50 years of peaceful protest had failed.[2] A statue of Suffragette Emmeline Pankhurst stands outside the Houses of Parliament today, but what would she think about the liberties being taken within? The limitations imposed by the state are neither natural nor inevitable; given a fundamental shift in thinking, we might be free of them entirely. Let us begin our subversive journey by testing the foundations upon which the state is built.

Democracy was invented in 594BC, when a peasant protest against the original Draconian law threatened to escalate into civil war. Solon of Athens introduced graded taxes, elections, and a legal system which was revolutionary in that both nobles and commoners were subject to it. Solon noted that his laws were not the best laws, only the best laws people would accept. Democracy began as a compromise. After two and a half thousand years of law-making and bureau-founding, we remain compromised.

Solon made another great contribution to Western culture. The father of democracy was also the father of the Greek pederastic tradition. Strange as it may seem, Heraclitus, Diogenes, and most Greek philosophers would take on a teenage lad to educate, and snuggle up behind him between lectures and knob him between the thighs. Philosophers wrote love poetry for their catamites. According to Plato, culture, love for humanity, peace and true spirituality begin with the love of a beautiful young man.[3]

Your good reverend is too much of a cultural relativist to impose his prudishly vanilla tastes upon long dead architects of morality – and besides, we owe a great deal to these august pederasts. But bear in mind that our political system derives from a philosophy that goes hand in hairy hand with the idealisation of men. (This was also the case amongst samurai, where boy-love had its own complex etiquette;[4] amongst Ming dynasty gentlemen;[5] and in the Islamic empire, where boy-love was a sign of culture, though morally complex – a thirteenth-century jurist commented that 'he who claims that he experiences no desire when looking at beautiful boys or youths is a liar, and if we could believe him he would be an animal, and not a human being.'[6]) Women did not come between Greek citizens discussing philosophy and matters of state, and nor did they vote, and our history is _his_-story, the story of great men, with women barely mentioned until recently. Our culture inherited an excess of order and rationalism, and some very weird power relations, where the buggers at the top still groom us, their charges, to take it lying down, grateful that we are part of the ideal system.

But does _demo kratis_ empower people?

More British young people vote on the _X Factor_ talent show than in general elections, and who can blame them?[7] I didn't vote for war in Iraq, I was on the street with millions who opposed it. I wasn't consulted about bank bailouts. My beloved Fukushima used to be modestly famous for its hot springs and peaches when I lived there at the turn of the century, but now it is internationally notorious for its radioactive ulcer, so I object to my taxes subsidising nuclear power – indeed, I pay tax only under duress. I never asked the state to kick homeless people out of empty properties. More fundamentally, beneath all the individually awful things the government does on my behalf, I never agreed to people I've never met and probably wouldn't like regulating my behaviour, even if it is for my own good, which I very much doubt. I never signed a social contract.

> Democracy is cancerous [noted William Burroughs]
> and bureaus are its cancer. A bureau takes root anywhere
> in the state, turns malignant like the Narcotic Bureau,
> and grows and grows, always reproducing more of its
> own kind, until it chokes the host if not controlled or
> excised. Bureaus cannot live without a host, being true
> parasitic organisms. (A cooperative on the other hand
> can live without the state. That is the road to follow. The
> building up of independent units to meet needs of the
> people who participate in the functioning of the unit.
> A bureau operates on opposite principles of inventing
> needs to justify its existence.)[8]

Narcotics Anonymous is a cooperative, composed of people with a stake in the issue, tackling a problem collectively. The Narcotics Bureau, by contrast, was mainly composed of agents left jobless when alcohol prohibition became untenable. Its legal fictions govern how we engage a whole class of substances which, according to a medical definition, alter physiology or perception (including anything from gin to ginseng, chamomile, codeine or ketamine in her cup).

Cocaine is defined by the state as a 'narcotic'. The two million Americans who spend about $70 billion a year on it may be punished more severely than paedophiles, with a

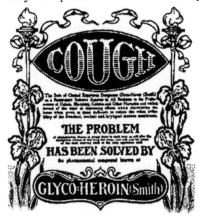

maximum penalty of life imprisonment.[9] Structurally related, and acting on the same receptors, is a drug with a $9 billion market. It has twice as many users as its cousin, many of whom use it almost daily, and nearly all of whom are children or teenagers.[10] But Ritalin® is legally defined differently, as a 'medicine'.

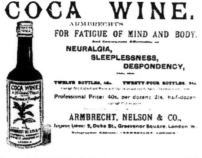

Drugs in this class may be recommended by family doctors to bring down your weight or your temperature, to keep your kids in line, and to keep you from worrying about it. You can also buy veterinary Prozac, from the 1-800-PetMeds website, which 'helps with obsessive compulsive behaviors such as tail chasing in dogs'.[11]

A third legal category comprises state-sanctioned recreational drugs (such as tobacco, alcohol and coffee). Nearly all of these are addictive, lucrative, and contribute to various harms, ranging from insomnia and heart disease to wife-beating. From a scientific perspective, the harms associated with alcohol and tobacco dwarf those of the illegal drugs, including crack and heroin. Some illegal drugs, including peyote, ganja and coca, have not been found to cause any tissue damage at all, and psychological harms have been massively exaggerated by media sensationalism.

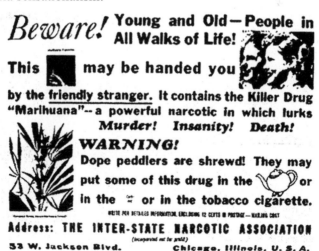

A rational harm scale was proposed in 2009 by Professor David Nutt, then head of the Advisory Council on the Misuse of Drugs (ACMD). He was sacked the same year for suggesting that policy did not follow science, and for his comments about horseriding being more dangerous than taking ecstasy.[12] Two more ACMD members resigned the following year, complaining that drug policy was dictated not by science but by sensationalist media reports; parliament responded by quietly removing from British law the troublesome clauses which stipulated that the ACMD be composed of trained scientists.[13] The state was equally cynical with cannabis in the 1930s and psychedelics in the 1960s: both were prohibited amid coordinated smear campaigns,[14] though the research indicated minimal harms and enormous potentials.[15]

When research was banned, the CIA continued to experiment, on nearly 1500 American soldiers and Viet Cong prisoners of war. Psychiatric patients were given LSD in combination with hypnosis, electrode implants and lobotomies,[16] and citizens were lured into experiments by prostitutes, where they were secretly drugged and observed.[17] At least one CIA employee, Dr. Olson, was spiked with acid in an observational study, and plunged to his death nine days later.[18]

The CIA was also busy trafficking hard drugs with crooked cops and politicians from the Golden Triangle to the Port of Buenaventura, funding bloody coups and contras with the profits. 'In my 30-year history in DEA [Drug Enforcement Agency],' commented Dennis Dayle, the head of Central Tactical Unit, 'the major targets of my investigations almost invariably turned out to be working for the CIA'.[19] Other DEA operations included a $4.7 billion dollar program spraying chemical defoliant over the Colombian Amazon and its inhabitants, in a failed attempt to root out coca growers.[20]

Police activities in the UK, like in the US, have 'no discernible impact on drug availability, price or purity'.[21] But when heroin prohibition was abandoned in Switzerland, addicts used less and committed fewer crimes, the country saved 45 francs per user per day, and the park once known as 'Needles Park' became safe for children to play in again.[22]

Laws, including drug laws, limit freedoms which cause little or no damage, but facilitate freedoms that no one should be granted. When fracking companies or Tesco move into an area where locals overwhelmingly oppose them, the state grants planning permission and subdues the ensuing riots.[23] We call this dream 'freedom': free trade, free speech, free elections, freedom from oppression, freedom of conscience, freedom of information. But what liberties are being taken with our freedoms?

How free is information in the UK? After the ten year media retrospective on the invasion of Iraq, most English adults underestimated by 100 times the number of Iraqis killed since, and only 2% responded correctly with a figure of around a million.[24] With carefully crafted soundbites and weighted reporting, inconvenient facts disappear from public consciousness. TV is employed to manufacture consent and complicity in atrocity, reminiscent of how Hitler used the radio. Like many cognitive modifiers, TV is probably not too serious on a physiological level if taken in moderation. But the average American uses it for over five hours every day, (which only a dedicated smack-head can match).[25]

What freedom is this bundle of restrictions, when I am not free to renounce it, and when over one in a hundred American adults are behind bars to preserve it?[26] Feudal lords derived their authority from physical power and a smattering of theology, but what underpins a state's monopoly on the use of violence? The rationalist state, if it is to distinguish itself from a protection racket, requires a philosophical or moral narrative behind the order it imposes. Rather than leaving us to muddle it out amongst ourselves, a cosmic dualism of Good

versus Evil is invoked. According to the blurb, the state works on our behalf for the Good – regulating trade, protecting our welfare, maintaining standards in education and hospitals and so on, while jailing Evil denizens at home and bombing Evil insurgents abroad.

Ω

The question of Evil is a knotty one. Back before I was called to the cloth, whenever the *chochemim* sat in debate at synagogue, whatever the topic, some impassioned old lady would invariably cry out: What about the question of Evil? It's all very well to live and let live, but what about those who want you to die? What about the Hitlers of this world?

A Jewish answer might note that Evil is complex, and that the Lord is ultimately responsible: 'I make peace, and create evil: I the LORD do all these things.'[27] Within the scope of one's own activities, however, sin (*khata*, literally to go astray) is rooted in man's 'evil inclination'.[28] Exactly what is sinful is laid down in the *Old Testament* and expanded upon over centuries of lively debate, but it requires both vigilance and redress.

As subsequent Abrahamic religions responded to the challenges that power and empire bring, Evil was personified with images cobbled together from various pagan deities; men were appointed to give instructions on good conduct. Imams decided which *hadith* (records of the acts and sayings of the Prophet) were authoritative, and these guide morality and underlie Islamic jurisprudence. In Christendom the supreme index of righteousness was faith (supplanting deed, which was central to Jewish religion). Faith in the Church became a matter of dogma and a key to salvation, and this included faith in the head of the Church. In the fourth century, when the Pope ordered those 'judaizers' keeping the fourth commandment by resting on the Sabbath to be excommunicated, that was that.[29] In 1997, when John Paul II cleared up any confusion about condoms by affirming the Catholic dogma that contraception is 'intrinsically evil',[30] that was that... until his successor amended this infallible decree, and decreed that condoms were 'a lesser evil' if used by men with HIV.[31]

We might laugh at this old Vatican relic, but to hundreds of millions, his word is an echo of God's, which carries considerable weight and generates plenty of guilt. Old-skool Protestants, on the other hand, and Christians of the Eastern Orthodox persuasion, traditionally view the Pope to be none other than the Antichrist himself – Evil personified! He is

surely more Evil (or at least less helpful) than a condom. But perhaps it is more charitable to think of him as an extremely delusional civil servant.‡

The question of Evil confronted me brutally when I was 16 and a drunk driver killed my friend and rendered another impotent only months after he had lost his virginity. Being of a theological bent, I concluded that if God existed, he must be Evil; but I later revised my position. If we have free will to drink excessively and drive dangerously, then we also have minds to measure risk and the will to avoid cars if we feel we should. The driver was not Evil so much as recklessly unskilful; and it is unskilful action that causes suffering, according to a Buddhist perspective. Karma, which means both 'action' and 'effect', is experienced collectively in some sense, like the weather. The wheel of karma rolls on, neither sentimental nor malicious, cutting tracks in the landscape, rolling over the toes of whoever stands in the way. It keeps you on your toes so that the toes crushed aren't yours. But sometimes toes get crushed all the same.

The Buddhist dodge is brilliant, but it relies upon a world where everything is suffering. 'Everything is suffering' is the first Noble Truth, the first thing the Buddha said after his enlightenment, and Japanese tradition remembers his dying words as 'what a sweet thing is life!' Suffering and sweetness are inseparable, as a beautiful lotus rising out of muddy water. When a woman falls at the claws of a lioness, her flesh feeds lion cubs. A picked pocket or decayed tooth demands attention, and calling thieves and bacteria 'Evil' doesn't help: that's what you get for not brushing your teeth. You will learn to pay attention, even if it takes 10,000 years of toothache in *samsara*.

---

‡ This 'lesser evil' quit his post, the first to do so in seven centuries; a few hours later the Basilica of St. Peter was struck by lightning. Twice.

His successor, to his credit, seems to be kinder and bolder; but regardless of the specifics of the doctrine, it is not healthy for your moral code to be dictated by anyone else – especially a celibate old man in a frock.

The Taoist answer is, of course, a story, which begins once upon a time in China when a horse ran away from its owner.[32] The old man's neighbours commiserated with him, but he answered them with a mysterious question: 'Who knows if it is good or bad?' Evil fortune turned to a blessing some time later, when the horse returned with a fine Barbarian stallion for him to take as his property. His neighbours congratulated him, but he stroked his wispy  beard and asked 'who knows?' When his son broke his hip riding the stallion, he answered grave-faced neighbours with his sagacious question again. Sure enough, when a Barbarian hoard came over the border, the old man's heir was spared service, while most of the men of his village were died in the fighting. 'What great luck!' cried his neighbours (for they were slow on the uptake).

Ω

Stanley Milgram went looking for answers to the question of Evil in the field of social psychology in 1961, against a backdrop of soul-searching with the trial of Adolf Eichmann, the mild-looking, pen-pushing architect of the Holocaust. His basic experiment begins with two subjects drawing lots to decide roles.[33] The 'teacher' subject then watches as the 'learner' subject is strapped into a chair and fitted with electrodes. Then the 'teacher' is taken to an adjacent room, and seated in front of a machine labelled 'Shock Generator'. He is asked to read a memory test to the learner through a microphone, punishing mistakes with increasingly strong electric shocks. Before the experiment begins, the technician gives the teacher a 45-volt shock as a taster.

When the first mistake is made, the teacher flips the first switch, labelled '15 volts – slight shock'. The machine buzzes, lights flash, a voltage meter swings, and the experiment continues. Each subsequent shock increases by 15 volts, and after the twentieth error and the 300-volt 'very strong shock', the learner is heard pounding on the wall. A technician explains that though shocks can be extremely painful, they cause no permanent tissue damage, and that 'the experiment requires that you continue'. When the next question goes unanswered, the technician explains that no answer is a wrong answer, and punishment should be given. More pounding follows the shock, but this is the last that is heard from the learner. The remaining questions go unanswered, and the teacher is asked to continue administering shocks.

The experiment was rigged to investigate the psychology of obedience. Though they drew lots, both lots read 'teacher'; the 'learner' was really a friendly middle-aged actor in league with the scientists. All 40 'teachers' continued until the pounding, at which point five rebelled. 65% continued through 'intense shock', 'danger – severe shock', to the maximum of 450-volts, marked simply 'XXX'.

Most teachers began to sweat or become visibly uncomfortable, and a third of them broke into nervous laughter. According to an observer:

> I observed a mature and initially poised businessman enter the laboratory smiling and confident. Within 20 minutes he was reduced to a twitching, stuttering wreck, who was rapidly approaching a point of nervous collapse. He constantly pulled on his earlobe, and twisted his hands. At one point he pushed his fist into his forehead and muttered: 'Oh God, let's stop it.' And yet he continued to respond to every word of the experimenter, and obeyed to the end.[34]

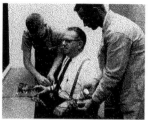

In follow-up interviews, many admitted they had believed the learner to be either dead or unconscious,[35] so what then of the question of Evil? Murder and torture are pretty nasty, but unless 65% of us are Evil, we must look for answers elsewhere. People are not 'Evil' with a capital E, a shiver down the spine and a cameo by Boris Karloff; but we are obedient, and our capitulation sucks Hitlers and Asaharas off the rubbish heap of human existence into positions of power. Hitler was a failed artist, lightly wounded in World War I and cured of psychosomatic blindness by a physician who filled him with Messianic delusions.[36] As chancellor, he was wired and paranoid from his daily amphetamine injection, but a whole nation of normal people obeyed him. Or rather, they obeyed the machine he directed. He did not design the system of government; he was voted in. From there, he merely fed into the existing system a dream of world domination for a humiliated and destitute population.

The chickens that used to wander past my shack in the Amazon would have found more food searching apart, but they stayed together because they were safer together. Like most social animals, humans are governed by unconscious imperatives; but we obey orders at a much greater distance, becoming, in some ways, *more* obedient as space increases, rather than less. In set-ups where the teacher was required to press the learner's hand against an electric plate, full compliance dropped to a third.[37] But when psychological distance was increased, and the teacher pressed a lever authorising an intermediary to administer the shock, 93% let him have it.[38] Milgram comments:

> When he merges his person into an organizational
> structure, a new creature replaces autonomous man,
> unhindered by the limitations of individual morality,
> freed of humane inhibition, mindful only of the
> sanctions of authority.[39]

It is tempting to think that the 1970s trimmed the claws of
the beast, but replications of Milgram's experiments over the
next 25 years showed no change whatsoever.[40] Our leaders still
point at something complex and call it something simple, like
'terrorism' or 'the Axis of Evil', and slaughter follows close
behind. Crusades are dreamt up by tragic, delusional people,
quaking in their shiny boots, their stoles and their old school
ties. First, opposing opinions are exterminated; then ordinary,
apparently non-delusional people follow the leader, goose-
stepping down the road to atrocity.

> If, in this study [asks Milgram] an anonymous
> experimenter could successfully command adults to
> subdue a 50-year old man, and force on him painful
> electric shocks against his protests, one can only wonder
> what government, with its vastly greater authority and
> prestige, can command of its subjects.[41]

If laws protect us from Evil, why did not one of a thousand
subjects threaten to call the police, or question the legality
of electrocuting a stranger?[42] We talk about 'law 'n' order',
like 'fish 'n' chips' or 'queen 'n' country', Siamese words
joined at the 'n', as if one implied the other. But order arises
spontaneously, in the waves of the sea and the patterns in jade.
Chaos and complexity carve repeated forms at different scales,
in coastlines and crystals, rivers and roots, and the rhythms of
the heart. The golden section, $1 : 1/2(\sqrt{5} + 1)$, measures out stems
along branches, knuckles along fingers, and the movements of
the planets. Single-celled creatures self-organise into optimal
fractal configurations. In the case of a living sponge, they
reform again after being pushed through a sieve.[43] We built
fractals into architecture long before mathematicians discerned

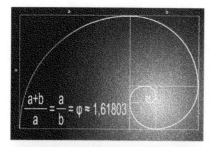

$$\frac{a+b}{a} = \frac{a}{b} = \varphi \approx 1,61803$$

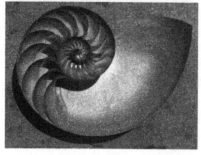

any laws governing them, because they are built into us. Birds sing fractal songs,[44] stocks rise and fall in fractal cadence.[45] Zipf's laws predict how sand falls into piles and how large cities grow,[46] how words are distributed through text[47] and how often academic papers are cited.[48] What laws do we need beyond these?

No overseer forces bees to make honey, no mountie marshals salmon up river, no flight controller plots bird migration. Crowds obey the formulae of fluid dynamics so closely that stadium designs can be tested on computers. Free individuals acting autonomously generate macro-order, whether single-celled creatures or stockbrokers. Instincts, which evolved over aeons in harmony with the planet, guide our behaviour, and learning is sufficient to order the rest. Children stop eating sweets when they feel sick, or remember the time they actually were sick.

Harmonious order, beyond that which is embedded in the fabric of the universe or our central nervous systems, arises not from law but from

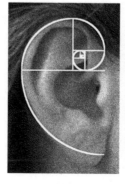

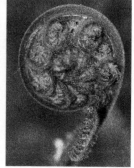

97

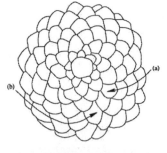

culture. There is very little drunken disorder in Italy, for example, where children grow up encultured with wine, drinking with their families; but the tightest drinking laws in Europe have not stopped British teenagers from binge drinking and misbehaving more than any of their European peers.[49] Regulations make fetishes of our vices, charging our choices with meaning, and sometimes encouraging the exact opposite of what they set out to stop.

Farmers plant in spring and harvest in autumn, without coercion. Governmental interference in agriculture does not create order but disrupts it. Over a million were driven to starvation and cannibalism under the Soviet collective agricultural policy,[50] and subsidies for maize in the US have encouraged monoculture over swathes of North America, to the detriment of local species, local economies, and the nutritional intake on a national scale. Imposing law to order the world as we would have it, rather than paying attention to how it is, we provoke nature into imposing order on us, as she will not accommodate disharmony indefinitely.

But wouldn't things get out of control without law? Things are already out of control! They always were. There is no fat controller. If someone was in control, perhaps he could stop people nicking my bicycle, or halt the cascade of events that leads to famine at one latitude and butter mountains a few degrees to the north. Control is an illusion, maybe even a pathology, judging by the behaviours exhibited by subjects in the Stanford prison experiment.[51] Given the uniforms and duties of guards and prisoners, normal healthy males were brutalising each other by Day 5, with humiliating tasks and bags over their heads. The research was aborted on Day 6, with one prisoner on hunger strike and several catatonic, and with kinder guards turning a blind eye to sadism. Worse still, everyone involved was under the impression that they were not free to leave, which was not the case. Sounds familiar?

There is no evidence that prisoners are reformed by being caged with like-minded folk, swapping skills and cultivating bitterness away from their friends, their family, and the opposite sex. The money spent on courts, coppers and clinks might be more effective elsewhere – such as building youth centres, for example, or decent housing. Despite all the measures to control it, crime has been increasing, generally speaking, since records began.[52] But homicides plummeted during the Great Depression, when everyone was on the same breadline.[53] The 30 most peaceful countries have the lowest inequality indices, and ten of the 11 most violent countries have the highest.[54]

99

Overcrowding, frustration and hunger encourage aggression in mammals, whether canine, feline, porcine, rodent or simian like us, but the inherently unstable nature of inequality may be even more fundamental than mammalian psychology. Two electrodes with the same charge will sit quietly near each other; but if the charge of one is raised, the system returns to equilibrium with a spark. Electrodes further apart can sustain a greater imbalance, but sooner or later sparks will fly, and all the more explosively.

The police, which George Orwell called 'the bodyguard of the moneyed class',[55] maintains this imbalance, but sparks are flying across the walls of gated communities all the same. Favela slums creep up the mountains of Rio de Janeiro, sharing idyllic views but not much else with the inhabitants of luxury walled condominiums, and kidnapping has become a way to bridge the gap. In South Africa, large, well-armed, super-violent gangs stage  guerrilla roadblocks and attack shopping malls.[56] Many murders involve money at some level, whether for insurance claims, in botched robberies or gang violence. Maybe the crimescape would be less bloody if the redistribution of unequal resources through stealing was easier?

According to *The Tao Te Ching*, 'if you overvalue possessions, the people begin to steal'.[57] Inequality breeds crime, which is a symptom of discord as much as a cause. In Japan, where low interest rates and relatively equal incomes keep imbalance in check, even the homeless have good shoes, and robbery and theft are extremely rare. At greatest risk are bras and knickers on the washing line, for which horny ninjas are willing to scale walls, and this reveals a less stable voltage. Perhaps it is the leftover influence of Confucianism, where the genders were separated from the age of 7 (because we are obedient over time as well as space, and the pronouncements of long-dead legislators still carry).[58] Or maybe it is that busy *salarimen* are too overworked to pursue normal relationships, but subway groping is endemic, with no-groping signs beside the no-smoking signs, and undercover cops riding trains in short skirts.

Sexual abuse is extremely rare amongst surviving matriarchies, like the Mosuo for example.[59] But nature restrained hardens into knots, whether the repressed urge is sexual desire, thrill-seeking, or ambition without an outlet other than a job at Starbucks. We are all born beautiful babies with breast fixations, but somewhere along the way something goes wrong, and some of us become rapists. The last thing on a rapist's mind is the law, and the average mugger is more concerned with their next crack pipe.[60]

Neither is your average mass murderer much concerned about the law, or easily policed. Independent bombers are, unlike many soldiers following orders, motivated by strongly held, often well-thought-out convictions. The Unabomber was a maths prodigy concerned about how technology limits our freedoms.[61] Whatever the merits of his method, others acting to expose this very real problem have turned fugitives of the US government.

The most active suicide bombers were the Tamil Tigers,[62] who had not Islamicist but secular objectives. Foreign troops on sovereign territory is a more accurate indicator than religion of the likelihood of such attacks.[63] Some bombers are also plain old, suicidally unhappy,[64] making an impact in one of the few ways still available in the hi-tech, homogenous and totally corporate culture supplanting traditional ways of life before their eyes. Islamic militants, junkies, miscreants and thieves are not the enemy; the enemy is that which seeks to regulate bogeymen at a distance, rather than confronting evil up close. Regulations regulate like a sewn up bumhole regulates diarrhoea.

Ω

101

On roads with neither street markings nor traffic lights, road safety improves dramatically. Lines, pavements and pedestrian crossings have been completely removed from many busy intersections, and several entire towns in Germany and Holland. The engineer boasts that there has never been a fatal accident on one of his roads.

> 'Who has the right of way?' he asked rhetorically. 'I don't care. People here have to find their own way, negotiate for themselves, use their own brains.'[65]

Lawless roads might not moderate the behaviour of the 15% who drive irresponsibly even when there are lines, but then what does? What can you do with people who are out of order?

You could, of course, lay a speed bump, if locals were empowered to use local knowledge to protect local interests. As things stand, lights, cameras and legal action for driving infraction do not prevent an astonishing 800,000 deaths per year in road accidents worldwide.[66] Perhaps an evolving etiquette of the truly open road would be less lethal. It would be chaos, of course. But order arises from chaos.

Ministers would be charged with serving policy rather than dictating it, in keeping with the word 'minister' (from *minus*, meaning less). In the *Tao Te Ching*:

> The best leaders are those their people hardly know exist...

> When they have accomplished their task, the people say, 'Amazing! We did it, all by ourselves!'[67]

What if parliament stuck to 'parlement' (speaking) and gave up the power to compel and punish, and the onus of being responsible for everything Good and Evil under the sun? It could be an administrational hub for discussing projects, whether roads or research or river conservation. And if people want to go and frack places, or disrupt fracking with their pitchforks, good luck to them! Perhaps, in the final analysis, it would be less hassle to pursue cleaner, more modest technologies to serve your needs, such as solar panels.

The law interferes with the emergence of organic order, intervening from Brussels in affairs between neighbours. If the Muggins boy is acting up, perhaps a friendly word to the family is the answer. Or maybe a short spell in the stocks. If it's not clear where the problem lies, or what the best thing to do is, then do nothing rather than something to worsen the situation. Leave the Muggins boy mugging until he tries to mug a kung fu master, and as the *Tao Te Ching* says, 'what is high up gets pulled down'.[68] Maybe we'll all learn kung fu, and walk each other home, and be happier for it? Power politics will arise, whatever the game, whatever the mammal; but at least we can play our games warm-blooded, amongst neighbours, and threaten each other without intermediaries whilst our children fall in love.

Would we all kill each other without 'law 'n' order'? Citizens kill each other anyway, law or no law. The Mexican vigilante movement has outpoliced the police, driving crime down by about 17%;[69] and most of the 1000–1500 murders per month that drove citizens to vigilantism in the first place were related to drug cartels, which command power precisely because the law prohibits their trade. Public beatings, makeshift jails and local chieftains bring their own problems, but would it be worse than our current crimescape and prison populations? Anarchism might not solve the problems that arise when people live together. It does, however, remove some of the impediments to addressing those problems from close up, in a measured fashion.

Perhaps left to our own devices we would not tear each other to shreds, but protect each other. Perhaps state welfare keeps us from faring well amongst ourselves. Benefits given lovelessly are received without gratitude, but a relatively rich man in a favela knows that his best security is generosity, maintaining the goodwill of his neighbours. Welfare was once a local affair, embedded into folklore, because no one wants desperate people in their communities, nor wandering between them. There were ample opportunities for the fortunate to support the less fortunate: the poor demanded figgy pudding from the wealthy with a song at festivals; Jewish farmers left the corners of fields unharvested for others; fools and jesters, clubfoots and village idiots brought luck to the village or protected the court from the evil eye. But whereas the Islamic custom is to leave excess produce at the marketplace, some supermarkets pour bleach on food just out of date, or lock up their bins to keep out bin-divers and avoid falling foul of health and safety laws.[70][71]

It is a rather feudal vision, but our cosmology has moved on a little from the Middle Ages, and we might do it differently. As things stand now, we are no less feudal than the Houses of Lancaster and York. Our feuds have only grown international, intercontinental, interhemispheric. If we must feud, let us do it locally, between neighbourhoods, or individuals – or better still, within our own skulls, confronting Evils we might have some chance of defeating, spanning more familiar hemisheres. Gandhi's final weeks are a testament to the unifying power of self-mastery. His hunger strikes halted sectarian violence, first in Calcutta and then in Delhi. His martyrdom, as he blessed his assassin, brought an end to the slaughter left in the wake of partition.

Gandhi hopped in and out of jail good-naturedly until the fall of the Raj. He was inspired by Henry David Thoreau, who wrote the magnificent *Civil Disobedience* while in jail for tax evasion. In it he argued that if one in ten men refused to bankroll slavery by withholding tax, the state would collapse under the weight of internees or change its policy; Massachusetts abandoned slavery shortly afterwards.[72]

'That government is best which governs not at all', wrote Thoreau, and 'when men are prepared for it, that will be the kind of government which they will have.'[73] But the state does not allow us to prepare ourselves. The police prevent us from policing ourselves, while shielding the wealthy from the consequences of inequality; but tension is rising. The whole rotten structure is ready to collapse with a gust of wind, and wind speeds are increasing. New Orleans was overwhelmed with looters when the waters of Hurricane Katrina retreated, having swept away the boundaries keeping the poor poor. If the law breaks down on a national or international level, with a world war, a pandemic or a zombie jamboree, it'll be so long to Solon and his band of merry buggers. Comrades and catamites! Organise, for anarchy is only three meals away, and not the books and bongs anarchy of the Ministry of Nem but the bricks and bombs anarchy of despair and disorder.

Order arises organically, and decays organically too; but some of our laws have lasted nearly 4000 years, since the Hammurabi code of ancient Babylon. If some vile substratum of our nature will inevitably manifest as a bully-boy mafia of some description, surely there are better ways to deal with it than by giving it title and executive power, and then delighting in tabloid reports of its indiscretions. While we cohabit with our corruption, and in the absence of clear answers, we can at least stop making it worse. We can invest our energies locally, where we can gain more purchase; and there is much to subvert close to home.

Mammals tend to obey protocols and follow scripts. This is the operating system of our species, so we had better learn to live with it. But we might learn to write scripts also, and follow Foucault's wise counsel, to 'put "in play", show up, transform, and reverse the systems which quietly order us about'.[74] The problem is not that we are programmed to follow, but that we have forgotten how to program, overwhelmed with redundant and corrupted code.

What good is changing the monkey in charge, through elections or revolutions, if we still can't lead ourselves? Even the idea that others are in charge cripples us. When I started planting vegetables and fruit trees around my housing estate, the first thing people asked was whether I had permission from the council. Of course not! The last thing the council did on the estate was confiscate the legs from the trampoline our kids were bouncing happily on. They don't live here, we do! So grab your shovel, and let's build a tyranny of the impassioned in place of a tyranny of the majority! And if you don't like them apples, you can chop the tree down yourself!

As pawns, we march along familiar tracks. The territory was claimed by bishops centuries ago, who brought their black-and-white gospel to every corner of the board on the point of a knight's lance. While certain laws have shifted over the centuries, we're still playing the same old game of coercion and control.

The endgame drags on as castles dominate lines of influence. Check. The Pope is not responsible for your soul. The government is not responsible for your behaviour. The policeman is not responsible for your safety. The doctor is not responsible for your health, nor the psychiatrist for your sanity. The scientist is not responsible for reality, and don't let him get away with it. Law makes you criminal, medicine afflicts you with syndromes, and none of this benefits anyone except the lumbering kings in the corners.

Check and check again. Our experiences are ours to interpret, messages written in strokes of pain and pleasure, and the gist is always the same: Pay attention! Keep checking! Test his formation, and trap his castle! Milgram repeated his experiment with a group of 'teachers' together, only one of whom was the real subject. When one of the actors refused to continue, 90% of subjects followed his example.[75] We obey until a better script becomes available – at which time nearly everyone will adopt it, even if it is authored by the subject rather than the scientist, by a pawn rather than a bishop. For authorship carries an authority of its own.

A pawn realises its potential when it breaks out of formation and pushes into new spaces and beyond, to the promise of transformation. A freethinking agitator need only issue orders less heartless than those he is subjected to. A full spectrum lies between the black and the white, so choose your shade and raise a banner.

Pawn takes castle, transforms into whatever he likes.

Checkmate in three.

6. THE MONK, THE MYSTIC AND THE MOSQUITO

To Bernard

'Ka ga imasu!' I complained, as the monk led me into a sparsely decorated temple hall. *'There are mosquitoes!'*

'Imasu ne,' he said simply and sagely. 'Indeed, they exist'; but I wasn't getting any sympathy from him, nor any chitchat. He bade me sit down in lotus facing the wall and picked up the *'kindly stick'*, a wooden rod used to beat distracted Buddhists. He lit a stick of incense, and I began to settle as he paced loudly behind me – *teku teku teku*, a pause as he turned, then *teku teku teku* as he paced back again.§ For a few minutes it was just the footsteps, the wall and myself (though the existence or otherwise of the latter is a matter for contemplation amongst Buddhists).

But then we were joined by a whine.

I could hear her meandering leisurely across the temple as her accomplice patrolled, ready to strike if I moved. *Teku teku*

---

§ The noise of a footstep. Japanese has great onomatopoeia.

teku… Pause… *Teku teku teku.* She landed on my neck, where I could almost feel her weight as well as her proboscis (I knew her to be female, as only females bite). There are many kinds of mosquitoes in Japan, including tiny, barely audible ones, long spindly fiends who stab through your jeans, and pretty black and white stripy ones. This was a particularly loud species – a big, slow-moving blood-tank, no doubt, adapted to temple life in symbiosis with the kindly stick, in a world where dinner sits still.

Unable to slap at her without completely disgracing myself and my country, I tried to concentrate on the *koan*, or Zen riddle the monk had given me at our previous meeting: 'Meaning is no meaning'. I had chosen to train at a Soto temple specifically because they do not use *koan*, which I suspected would not help me. My mind is full of questions, but I can't imagine thinking about one constantly for years, to the exclusion of everything else. The monk had given me one anyway. 'Meaning is no meaning'. It meant precisely nothing to me, and I had directed my focus towards the wall in the normal Soto manner. Since that first session, however, spring had sprung to life with a chorus of insects. My concentration was one-pointed on the one drinking my blood. *Teku teku teku.*

She began speculating around my face and forearms. With my eyes half-open in the traditional Zen manner, at the edge of the internal and external worlds, I could follow her movements as she descended to settle on my wrist. She sat motionless as the Buddha as I squirmed without and within. *Teku teku teku.* How did Gautama's tradition of sitting meditation arise in a mosquito-infested land? Is there more wisdom in the whirl of the Dervish? *Teku teku teku.* Is the incense there to help keep the bastards away? I remembered the mosquito I had pursued at length in Mexico to take alive for a blood sacrifice, and considered the wheel of karma as it turns. *Teku teku teku.* Could I bring a mosquito net next time?

Many tense breaths later, she disengaged and I breathed a mindful sigh of relief. My attention returned to the wall and began to concentrate, one hand resting in the other, tips of the thumbs touching. She buzzed around for a moment and landed on the base of my thumb. Her desire was the root of suffering, and insatiable as that of a hungry ghost! *Teku teku teku*. Show some self-restraint in the temple, for the Buddha of Compassion's sake! *Teku teku teku*. What impertinence, to bite the acolyte three times, and to feed at the one spot where a tiny adjustment of the hand mudra would bring her oblivion.

What a riddle you pose, little *roshi*! The first Buddhist precept forbids taking life, but I have taken no precepts. The fourth noble truth is to meditate upon the paths, and you disturb my meditation. It is said that if you meet the Buddha on the path, kill him; but what of the mosquito? If the Buddha is everywhere, then he is in the mosquito also, which I meet here, vexing me on my path. Am I to kill her, then? The rabbis were debating in the temple as the mosquito supped... *teku teku teku*... and supped... *teku teku teku*. I waited for the monk's footsteps to pause... *teku teku teku*... and unleashed the one-pointed devastation of my Shaolin Buddha finger.

Squish...

... *teku teku teku*...

...smack. The kindly stick came down on my shoulder.

It is a relief when it comes. Also called the silent yell, the strike reminds you where you are and what you are doing. The pain in the legs evaporates, and the story in your head melts away. With my nemesis now a satisfying red smear, I finished the session in peace, enjoying the beatific bliss of a successful kill under difficult circumstances.

Twenty minutes later, I sat rubbing my aching legs as the monk chain-smoked cigarettes in less formal monkish get-up.

I asked why he used *koan* in a Soto temple. He ignored my question and asked what Japanese food I liked. I questioned him about how to deal with mosquitoes. He asked what sports I play. He was either being very Zen or very Japanese, or both. Almost every time I met a new Japanese person, whether a schoolkid or section chief at city hall, these two rather formal questions would be asked of me. Adults almost invariably followed that with, 'Do you like saké?'

Many Japanese monks seem more like civil servants than holy men, and the position passes from father to son. I once asked a pupil if he wanted to be a monk like his father, and he explained that he wanted to be a baseball player, but if he didn't make it he would become a monk.

The monk before me seemed pleased that I liked cycling. 'Do you like saké?' he asked.

Japan is one big *koan* sometimes, with everyday banalities tugging at the stitches of the tapestry in your head. Despite the Buddhist precept to avoid drink and drugs that befuddle the mind, I have sometimes enjoyed the company of drunken monks – including once after a lecture on Tibetan Buddhism, where they slurred and boasted until their red-faced drunken master stumbled into a taxi. The minute he left, most present reached into their robes for their cigarettes (having denied themselves temporarily out of respect for the traditional Tibetan teachings advising against smoking).

Yes, I like saké. Do you like saké? I like cycling. And Aikido. I do not like football. I like sushi, but I do not like octopus sushi. Meaning is no meaning. I do not like mosquitoes. How about you?

Everyone hates mosquitoes, but mosquitoes love us. They view a scholar, a villain and a Jehovah's Witness without distinction, looking beyond the skin to the treasure within. Ka-sensei has a lot to teach us, more than cuddly bunny rabbits, and more than the Archbishop of Canterbury. Where they exist, these ankle fetishists serve as a very persistent reminder of our place in the universe and the food chain. We imagine, to our continuing suffering, that the cosmos revolves around us. The mosquito knows we are here to satisfy her.

In the Mexican rainforest, mosquitoes form a cloud around you wherever you go, and babies spend their first months crying until they become accustomed to the onslaught. I used to teach lessons to a slow, constant round of applause as the students slapped at their parasites. The teacher before me fled within a week of arriving, but I stuck it out for three weeks, swelling into a big red itchy mess. Scratching merely turns the wheel of suffering and samsara, and if you are really unlucky you might end up with a bacterial colony eating into your flesh. The bite of the mosquito teaches the virtue of non-action. Turn the mind to another object and it will pass as it arose.

Unless, of course, you get malaria.

Malaria is more than just irritating; it is the biggest killer on the planet, taking more than two lives per minute. But like the mosquito, it has its place in the grand scheme of things. It protected us from ourselves for millennia. Attempts to develop the rainforests had always been doomed to feverish failure until the stakes were upped with World War II, and battle commenced in the bloodstreams of soldiers. Two principal weapons were developed against malaria: the prophylactic chloroquine, and DDT, the first pesticide. After the war a chemically enhanced Bigfoot was unleashed, cutting highways for logging, farming, mining and settling. The WHO Global Malaria Eradication Programme began in 1955, speeding up the destruction, and by 1962, 1% of the Brazilian Amazon had been cleared. Today 20% is lost,[1] and over half of the Nepalese forest had been destroyed.[2] Rainforests shelter half of the species on the planet; we breathe the oxygen they produce. Today malaria kills more than ever before and drug resistance is spreading, but humanity continues to grow, parasitically and to the detriment of most other species, at the rate of 80 million new souls per year.

Ka-sensei held us in an irritating balance, and we scratched our way out. Order arises organically in the world. Meaning is imposed. Malaria kills. I don't like malaria. It is bad. I like chloroquine. It saves lives. It is good. I don't like mosquitoes. I like DDT. It is good... or is it? Meaning changes. It soon became clear that DDT accumulates at the top of the food chain and kills more than just mosquitoes. The iconic American bald eagle had dwindled to 500 individuals throughout the continent by 1972, when DDT was banned in the US. The bald eagle has started to recover since; but DDT is still used in many countries, including Brazil, where I am presently editing in a rainforest shack, swiping at the mosquitoes buzzing around me, with a pus-filled wound on my chest from the bite of a sandfly. I still don't like mosquitoes; but that is my problem, not the entire biosphere's.

We are inextricably linked to our environment, some of which irritates us, but it is still part of us. We doctor the world around us according to the meaning we impose upon it, which is fleeting. The damage can last incalculable aeons of lifetimes.

Earlier attempts to control pests involved importing their natural predators, such as the mosquitofish, the common starling and the cane toad, which were introduced to Australia. The logic is solid, as far as it goes; but the rest of the eco-system was not factored in. All three invasive species out-competed native species, driving them to extinction or the endangered list. Cane toads become a plague which is advancing across Australia, killing cane beetles among other species, starving the creatures that once ate them, and also poisoning predators with its toxic secretions. It also spreads salmonella.[3]

Other initiatives for different ends have been similarly disastrous. Back in the 1890s, American rude mechanicals imported birds for poetic reasons, specifically those mentioned by Shakespeare.[4] As a result, the sweet song of the common starling is today heard throughout the continent, silencing indigenous species wherever it went, as well as destroying crops. A short-sighted British rationalist decided to cultivate Nile Perch for fishing in Lake Victoria in the 1950s, and by 1980 it had taken over 80% of the lake's biomass and wiped out over a hundred fish species.[5] In 1990, the African killer bee was introduced to Texas to boost honey production; it hybridised with local bees, and the highly aggressive result is presently advancing north.

It sounds completely deranged to deliberately introduce killer bees to your country, but our current meddlings are on a

The great expectations held for DDT have been realized. During 1946, exhaustive scientific tests have shown that, when properly used, DDT kills a host of destructive insect pests, and is a benefactor of all humanity.

Pennsalt produces DDT and its products in all standard forms and is now one of the country's largest producers of this amazing insecticide. Today, everyone can enjoy added comfort, health and safety through the insect-killing powers of Pennsalt DDT products . . . and DDT is only one of Pennsalt's many chemical products which benefit industry, farm and home.

different scale. Biochemists have turned their cataracts towards the genetic code, but how much do we actually know about genetics? The Human Genome project investigates only the DNA sections called 'sense'. The other 90% is called 'nonsense' or 'junk', because it doesn't mean anything to biochemists; they assume its role is purely structural. We are left with a parts list coding for proteins, but no instruction manual. We have very little idea how the proteins are put together, or how the order of expression changes in such a precise and responsive manner; but scientists feel confident enough to modify the code and release their creations from the lab, assuring the public that their spread can be controlled. In their gargantuan arrogance, they have forgotten that plants are essentially well-evolved DNA dispersal machines. While transgenic ingredients compete on supermarket shelves, transgenic grasses and other species have escaped and hybridised, and compete in the wild.[67]

Other executive decisions are being taken over which humans may be born. The genetic screen is already filtering out foetuses with thalassaemia and Down's syndrome. What deviation from the norm is next on the list? Given the information and the choice, some expectant parents might well choose to terminate pregnancies of disabled babies. An argument has already occurred over a deaf foetus;[8] who is next to find that their life means nothing? I had the pleasure of teaching a 'special needs' class in Japan, but they were the real teachers – natural, impulsive, friendly, and mostly happy; the exact opposite of normal teenagers. Might there be no more retarded people to see through the dry dust of etiquette one day, or no more autistics with Buddha-like intensity of concentration? Could humanity be rationalised at the embryonic stage?

Rationalism has been rationalising society since the seventeenth century, when various groups not meeting the standards of the Age of Reason began to be incarcerated, including paupers and the insane. Before this, the village idiot, for whom meaning was quite different from conventional standards, was often considered closer to God. 'Raiseth thou a cry against madness? By thy life, thou shalt have need of it' warns *The Talmud*,[9] and the merry madness continued into *Corinthians*, where 'the foolishness of God is wiser than men'.[10] There was a rich tradition of holy madmen in Europe, as in other traditions: St. Sabas spent the day in a dungheap; St. Andreas drank from puddles and slept naked outside with the dogs; St. Simeon threw peanuts at the church congregation and dragged a dead dog around.[11][12] Even St. Francis preached in his birthday suit.[13]

Patients begin conversations with my friend the psychiatric nurse with lines like 'You know, time doesn't exist.' And they are right. Neurotics are often, as William James noted, intelligent, obsessive pattern-seekers, thinking outside the normal assumptions. 'If there were such a thing as inspiration from a higher realm, it might well be that the neurotic temperament would furnish the chief condition of requisite receptivity.'[14] My beloved and serially sectioned granny used to take me on her knee and tell me all about what the races on other planets were like, what they traded between themselves, and the messages they send to us. My parents weren't very happy about it, but my first Fisher Price alternative cosmology provided protection from the heavy shades of the rational universe that teachers, newsreaders, and other right-thinking people were peddling.

The label 'insane' depends entirely on where one draws one's lines, and even professional psychiatrists draw carelessly. In one study, a professor sent students to eight mental institutions across the US, where they mimicked madness by claiming to hear the word 'thud'. This was the only symptom expressed.[15] All were diagnosed and admitted, and despite the plants explaining that the 'thud' had ceased immediately after admission, the average period of incarceration was 19 days.

One hospital responded by challenging the professor to send more; he agreed and specified the month. Though no plants were sent that month, the hospital erroneously declared that 20% of 193 genuine applicants were frauds. And so psychiatrists concluded that the problem must be human error. Questionnaires were designed to diagnose disorders. They detected mental disorders in over 50% of normal Americans.[16]

Mental disorders, psychedelic experiences, and other excursions from the bounds of normality are very rarely dangerous to anything except the status quo. Bizarre ideas and compulsions question our assumptions regarding reality, and that is why they are policed. According to R. D. Laing:

> The statesmen of the world who boast and threaten that
> they have Doomsday weapons are far more dangerous,
> and far more estranged from 'reality' than many of the
> people on whom the label 'psychotic' is affixed.[17]

But statesmen are not the only threats, and neither are killer bees, nor the honey-monsters breeding them. Short-sighted rationalists carve up the world like a gang of necrophiliacs sawing up a corpse, each having his wicked way with a different hunk of flesh. Physicists create technology to generate nuclear waste for their great-grandchildren. Businessmen suck with all their might on the breasts of the goddess, oblivious to her changing expression, pulping ancient Tasmanian forests for Japanese serviettes, battering and frying Atlantic cod to the edge of extinction, growing rich selling perch from the Lake Victoria catastrophe.

Meaning morphs as the picture unfolds, but the rational mind thinks only as far as it understands. Rational conclusions are surmised from what is known, which is at best a rough sketch of the world, and at worst a lonely and paranoid hall of delusions. Meaning begins in a brain, where bias is built into linguistics and programmed into our neurobiology, where Bacon's idols and the gods of coercion distort the shadows on the wall. But the world outside of the cave is more complex than any mind within can fathom.

In Tibetan Buddhist funeral rites, the cycle of birth and death is honoured by leaving monks' corpses out on towers, but today they rot slowly as there are not enough vultures to eat them. The DDT tragedy is being repeated with Diclofenac, a drug used in cattle farming, which proved to be toxic to vultures. Since it was introduced in the early 1990s, the vulture population has plummeted by over 95%,[18] but despite the explosion of rotting animal carcasses all over the subcontinent, the drug is still sold in 92% of veterinary stockists in Pakistan.[19] Once again, in 2008, the WHO embarked on a massive anti-malaria program, with insecticides sprayed inside houses and impregnated into free mosquito nets. This shortsighted charity kills other insects as well as mosquitoes, impoverishing food chains, and it can't be very good for the humans sleeping inside the nets. The program will cost around two billion dollars per year until... *teku teku teku*... until further notice, because even the WHO has admitted that malaria can't be eradicated. The first eradication program nearly wiped out malaria in Sri Lanka, but not quite; and so a generation of children grew up unexposed, and without developing immunity. The result was a massive resurgence, which today claims 10,000 victims each year.[20]

Meaning is no meaning, but with all this irritation buzzing around our heads, do we have the patience to sit still and meditate on the riddle before settling on the answer? How many slaps from the kindly planet do we need before we fix our dreadful posture? Can you hear the footsteps approaching across the temple? ... *teku teku teku*... The kindly stick is raised to strike, my fellow novices, but on whose neck will it fall? ... *teku teku teku*... The itch is becoming intense, but can we remain still, and keep our minds and bodies in check? ... *teku teku teku*... Can we work through the riddle? ... *teku teku te*...

...*ku.*

7. FROM LAYERED TRUTHS
TO HORNS AND HOOVES:
EXU'S JOURNEY

To the other devilish Dan

For thousands of years in Yoruba lands, families gathered around the fires, backs to the cold West African night, singing songs and telling stories of their gods, the *orixas*, and their counterparts, the *ajogun* or agents of mischief. The trickiest of all is Exu, who straddles the boundary, being both an *orixa* and the leader of the *ajogun*.

In one story he walks the trail between two farms, sharing his brilliant wit with one farmer, then later with the other. The farmers meet at sundown, according to their custom, and discuss the remarkable fellow. One remarks on his black hat; the other insists it was red. The argument escalates until they are at each other's throats, and then Exu arrives and doffs his hat, which is black on one side and red on the other. A difference of perspective had become a dispute over truth. When minds are not broad enough to contain different points of view, right and wrong are defined along the edge of the fields we toil, along

Papa Legba image above courtesy of Nemo Boko

national, habitual or ideological lines, and conflict follows swiftly behind.

Ambiguous at the boundary, revealing truth with his deceits, Exu is both male and female, and sculpted with the parts of both. He is also both prince and beggar, limping along with one foot forging ahead in the world beyond and the other dragging behind in the material. His arrival forces harmony upon the small mind with a crack, hijacking ill-conceived programs at the outset, and holding things up until balance has been established.

Exu is neither good nor bad, neither this nor that; but he is potent. His name is pronounced 'Eshu' (and the *orixas* are 'orishas') but how handsome he looks in his bow-X-tie. In the Yoruba language he is Elegba (*ele*, the messenger, of *agbara*, authority). He will pass your message on to higher forces, and facilitate your desires; but he is ruthless. He topples walls to crush people standing in stupid places.[1] He hides snakes in the grass at the crossroads, and sells cures to the victims as they limp into the marketplace. The market, with its routine of communication, exchange and trickery, is his domain, as is the crossroads. He is present at any site of transmission, and he is there in the lover's bed. He hides in the shadows of the liminal zone, emerging to make a painful point or leave a curious gift. Problem and solution, loyal friend and treacherous enemy, Exu is feared and revered in equal measure, but not to be forgotten.

Where stories are not carved into stone, there are other endings to the same beginnings, even other beginnings. In one version of the tale, Exu leaves the farmers to fight, and the brawl escalates into full-scale war between their villages. Exu finally appears to stroll amongst the smouldering ruins, smiling in satisfaction. The trickster is a shape-shifter and tale-weaver, ambiguous wherever he emerges, and Bible stories retain something of these paradoxes. Jacob wrestles all night with a violent assailant, and finds him to be God in the morning. Satan (the Hebrew word for 'adversary') is authorised by Jehovah to terrorise the sinless Job, and the Lord describes King Nebuchadnezzar, the genocidal conqueror of Jerusalem, as 'my servant'.[2]

Through the vicissitudes of history, a wedge was driven between the two sides of the mystery. *The Bible* was deployed as a moral and legal code to serve the ends of empire, but the patriarchs are neither moral nor lawful: Abraham pimps his wife;[3] Lot tries to pimp his daughters,[4] and ends up bedding them;[5] Jacob scams his starving brother,[6] and later his blind father.[7] All these acts are rewarded by the Lord, whose purposes they serve, and the harshest punishment is reserved for outsiders who dare to mix with the Chosen. For example, in one episode a Hivite prince, whose 'soul clave unto Dinah the daughter of Jacob', invites the Israelites to stop wandering and live amongst them. The Israelites agree on condition that the Hivite men circumcise themselves. The Hivites acquiesce, so three days later the Israelites invade, massacring the men 'when they were sore', and stealing their animals, their wealth, their women and their children.[8] Even this carnage was not enough after a similar genocidal raid. 'Have ye saved all the women alive?' cried Moses, wroth at the half-arsed massacre. Kill them all, he insisted, and only 'the women children, that have not known a man by lying with him, keep alive for yourselves'.[9]

Whereas the English word 'evil' suggests serial killers or dark forces, the Hebrew word translated as 'evil' (*ra*) has no moral undertones. It can mean, for example, food that has gone rotten, as in two instances of *ra* in the verse describing '*naughty* figs, which could not be eaten, they were so *bad*.'[10] Even Jehovah is about to do 'evil' by destroying the Israelites, until Moses persuades Him to change His mind.[11]

A closer reading does reveal a dualism in *The Old Testament* – but between Jew and gentile, rather than good and evil. Jehovah states over 50 times in *Leviticus* that the law is 'between Him and *the children of Israel*'.[12] Laws for Jews and non-Jews living amongst them were different,[13] with three capital exceptions: slandering the Jewish God, disrespecting the Jewish sabbath, and killing a man (in practice, a Jew).[14] One of the gravest punishments was to be cast out of the tribe.[15]

Biblical prohibitions often reinforce this dualism, rather than protect any moral standard. There is nothing intrinsically evil about a foreskin, for example, nor anything immoral about sharing foods and daughters with neighbouring tribes. Those rules did, however, prevent the Jewish people from dissolving into the surrounding non-kosher tribes for over three millennia, which is almost unique in history.

The difference between Chosen and unchosen is simple, but good and evil is complex in *The Bible*, and Jehovah takes responsibility for both: 'I form the light, and create darkness: I make peace, and create evil: I the Lord do all these things'.[16] The deity is morally inconsistent, to say the least, and different names of God make pronouncements at odds with each other.

Emerging from this ambiguous story, a transgressive becomes the principal figure in *The New Testament*. His rout of the moneychangers[17] and rows with Pharisees challenge social conventions. When he suggests that he who is without sin cast the first stone at an adulteress,[18] the people of an angry mob look sheepishly at one another and quietly abandon Mosaic Law. Jesus breaks laws regularly, often simply because he is peckish, abandoning religious fasts,[19] snacking on the priestly bread,[20] and allowing his disciples to pick corn on the Sabbath, which is a capital crime.[21] He bids a man shirk his religious duty to his dead father, saying 'let the dead bury their dead; but go thou and preach the kingdom of God'.[22] For Jesus, as for

Exu, the message is what is important, and boundaries are for the breaking.

In Church iconography, Christ almost universally appears helpless, as a babe in arms, a victim pinned to the cross, or a corpse in the *pietà*. Otherwise he is being whipped and humiliated around the walls of the church and the stations of the cross, but his stories describe a firebrand, with a bullwhip in his hand[23] and a trail of arguments behind him.[24] Coming to promote not peace, 'but rather division',[25] he resists convention and insults the authorities until his final breath, when he questions even God himself.[26] His anarchist alternative to *Leviticus* comprises only two principles:

> The first of all the commandments is, Hear, O Israel;
> The Lord our God is _one Lord_. And thou shalt love the
> Lord thy God with all thy heart, and with all thy soul,
> and with all thy mind, and with all thy strength.[27]

This is explicitly anti-dualistic, demanding love for the singular force that reigns supreme over good and evil.

> And the second is… Thou shalt love thy neighbour as
> thyself. There is none other commandment greater than
> these.[28]

Law is nearly always mentioned in a bad light in *The New Testament*. The most commonly exalted virtue in *The New Testament* is charity, but *agape* is not money in tins or feeding the poor *per se*, but rather neighbourly love, forgiveness, understanding, goodwill and tolerance in judging others.[29] Exu's stroll between the fields warns of the consequence of intolerance, of insisting that your viewpoint trumps your neighbour's. Law divides, but charity breaches the boundary between self and other.

Jesus also breaks the laws of physics with his transmutations and water-walking. Though typical of Jewish prophets in many ways, his miracles, like his rebellious streak, are new. The miracles of Moses and other prophets are all explicitly acts of God, but Jesus heals and turns water to wine with his own hands, blurring the boundary between God and man. Jewish scripture never describes God as a father, but Christ calls him 'father' hundreds of times. When he goes as far as saying 'I and the Father are one', people throw stones at him.[30]

This fisherman has something decidedly fishy about him, something foreign in fact. In the first few centuries of our Saviour, our Saviour was not the only saviour in town. A character breaching the boundary between the human and divine worlds was called a *hero* in Greek. Hercules, Theseus and Perseus were all heroes, born to divine fathers and human mothers; like Jesus, all three struggled with the limitations of the flesh, and were glorious in death. The image of a god or hero bound and tortured at the crossing-point between the worlds is common in pagan mythology. Theseus and Hercules were bound, as was Prometheus, who stole the sacred fire. In Norse mythology, both Odin and his brother and enemy Loki were bound and mutilated. The theme of chastity also tends to arise in the myths of the hero's mother: Danaë, mother of Perseus, was locked away from men by her father; Aethra, mother of Theseus, was impregnated by Poseidon on her wedding night, when still a virgin.

Adonis is, in many ways, a dead (and risen) ringer for Jesus. He hails from the Middle East, bearing the Semitic name of Lord (the same root as Adonai). His mother Myrrha, whose name recalls Maria, went on to be transformed into a Myrrh tree, which was one of the gifts of the Kings of the Orient, and the ancient grove shading Bethlehem was sacred to Adonis. Bethlehem means 'the house of bread', and Adonis was the spirit of corn, from which bread was made,[31] where Jesus was 'the bread of life'.[32] Like Christians, Adonis worshippers sought salvation through the blood of a sacrifice. So did the devotees of Mithras, another saviour God born surrounded by shepherds.

Even in a country as Christian as Brazil, our natural tendencies are towards paganism. My favourite Brazilian begins her day with a *Pai Nosso*, an *Ave Maria*, and a big friendly *'Bom dia Jesus!'* to the rising sun (when she is lucky enough to see it rising over London). The sun still stains the sky red as it dies at dusk, and rises immortal again in the morning, and such potent poetry does not die easily. Jesus was already associated with the sun and sun-gods in the semi-pagan Gospels, with the virgin birth and the 12 apostles for the 12 houses the sun passes through. Christ continued to absorb attributes from his semi-divine peers. In 354AD, his birthday was set at December 25th, along with Mithras, Adonis and other solar heroes. This date in the old Julian calendar was the morning after the longest night of winter, when the sun begins to dominate again and one year crosses into the next. It was celebrated with the pagan feast of Sol Invictus (the unconquered sun).

December 25th was also the day the constellation of the virgin appears over the horizon. *The Bible* does not mention when Jesus was born. The only clue is that the shepherds were

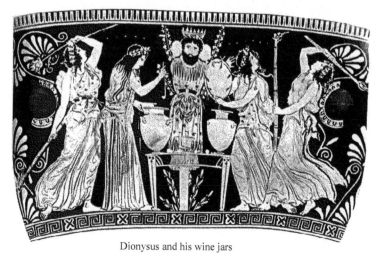

Dionysus and his wine jars

125

out in the fields, watching their flocks[33] – and even Church fathers conceded that sheep were kept inside during cold December nights.[34] The earliest reference to Christ's birthday on the solstice was in 354AD,[35] set there to compete with Mithraic festivities on that day; Christianity had ousted Mithraism as state religion only 30 years previously, and was consolidating its hold over Rome. A decade later, church authorities fiddled the calendar again, moving the day of worship to Sunday, the day of the Sun gods, including Mithras.[36] Any 'judaizers' busted resting on the Sabbath were branded as anathema,[37] and so obeying the fourth commandment became punishable with excommunication.

Things changed as Rome became Christianised and Christianity was institutionalised. Constantine the Great saw a vision of the cross superimposed upon the sun, so his hagiography goes, and heard a divine command to conquer under this symbol.[38] He obeyed, and had the sign painted on military banners, and so the Emperor who was revered as a pagan god in his lifetime was canonised as a Christian saint after death, despite having had his son poisoned and his wife boiled alive.[39]

Under Constantine, the cross became a symbol of power. It had previously been a symbol of luck amongst Christians, as it was for neighbouring pagans; before that, its Christian significance, if any, is unclear. The word translated as 'cross' in the gospels is 'stauros' (from histemi, to stand), which in Classical Greek meant a stake. It may have also meant 'cross', and while scholars disagree over the matter, scripture leaves us none the wiser. A scholarly apologist comments, in a defense of the traditional Christian interpretation, that 'the word stauros does generally mean stake rather than cross, but, according to every source I've come across, there was no Greek word for cross.'[40]

Along with the inconclusive language, the evangelists provide sparse details of the scene; and while the Romans did crucify some criminals, no contemporary account mentions a cross. Tacitus (*c*.56AD – 120AD) recalls that Christus, leader of the Christians 'suffered the extreme penalty ... at the hands of ... Pontius Pilatus',[41] though what exaclty the penalty was remains unclear. In *The Talmud*, Yeshua was stoned and then either hanged or impaled on a stick.[42] The language is typically vague, but there is certainly no cross, and nor is there any nailing. Early Christians worshipped in their churches under the symbol of the fish, not the cross. The first unambiguous mention of the cross in Christian writings is in 201, when Tertullian wrote that 'we Christians wear out our foreheads with the sign of the cross.'[43] He also admits that there is no scriptural basis for the superstition.[44] The earliest known crucifixion scene dates from the fifth century.[45] Until then, the cross and crucifixion are 'curiously missing' from images, according to one esteemed Christian art historian.[46]

Despite making a career of attacking pagan superstitions, Tertullian did not mention the pagan roots of the cross, which run deep. A shape like the letter T was the symbol of Tammuz, the divine shepherd and dying saviour of Mesopotamia, who descended into the underworld to emerge again on the winter solstice. In Egyptian art, priests and gods hold the ankh cross in their hands, and sun-worshipping pharaohs were mummified with their arms crossed over their chests. This position, which convent children are still

Pre-Columbian pottery

Ethiopian tattoo

Neolithic cave art

Neolithic stamp

taught to sleep in today, is the sign of Osiris, another dying and resurrected god, and god of bread and wine. Some Ethiopian Christian sects still tattoo the cross on their heads, which is a fully pagan tradition; tattooing is prohibited in *The Bible*. The cross was painted on tents and offered to rivers in Algeria, Tanzania, across the desert to Niger,[47] and on to the lands of the Yoruba, to the master of the crossroads and the double-cross.

Older still is the swastika, found at prehistoric sites from the British Isles to China, and in Neolithic India. The sun-cross of Constantine's vision (a cross within a circle) is found on Bronze Age artefacts[48] and North American aborigine art, and the Aztec Quetzalcoatl bears the sun-cross on his shield. This hero, born to a virgin in some of his myths,[49] descends to the underworld, and spans the worlds with his snake belly scraping the sand and his feathers to the sky.[50] Both the cross and crosser are universal forms, appearing even in the absence of direct transmission. Heroes born of mortal and immortal parents appear all over the world, from Gilgamesh of Uruk to Merlin of Albion.

Back in Africa, the crossroads was sacred to Exu when the virgin mother was still in pigtails. Ritual opened and closed with the messenger and the cross many centuries before the legend of Christ, and still whenever any *orixa* is petitioned, some liquor or a cigar is first offered in sacrifice to one of the Exus, for the *orixas* can only be reached through the figures at the boundary. And God can only be reached through Jesus:

> I am the door... I am the way, the truth, and the life: no
> man cometh unto the Father, but by me.[51]

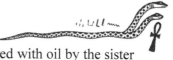

Jesus is sacrifice personified, anointed with oil by the sister of Lazarus, and thus made messiah (literally 'the anointed one'). Oil is also poured on Exu's sacred mounds.[52] Libations are made at boundary zones, at the shore or the riverbank, where many of Jesus' miracles happened; they are made at the town gate or up a hill, recalling Jesus's sacrifice at Calvary, on a hill at the edge of the city.

The heretic and healer Yeshua met a nasty end on a stick of some description; Jesus Christ Superstar rose from the dead to become the centrepiece of a cosmology that stretches across time and space, spanning land and culture and empire, from before Adam and into eternity. The figure morphed rapidly as stories were retold, with facts, figures and teachings changing even between different gospels. The reinterpretation continued, through the epistles of *The New Testament*, and the papal bulls(hit) that regimented worship in a succession of empires.

There is surely treasure buried deep beneath this X, but can we dig up anything more than cross-ponderances? Did the archetype arise in different places? How much did the cults influence each other as they spread? What changes when crosses cross and minds intertwine?

Exu is legion, with two sides and 21 faces. There is an Exu for every person, and an Exu for every family and clan, just as there were *genii* in Rome. There is even an Exu for every Exu. By contrast, Jesus is considered to be the only Son of God:

Quetzalcoatl

> The beginning of the gospel of Jesus Christ, the *[sic]*
> Son of God[53]

The Greek definite article (similar to the word 'the' in English) appears in this verse, but not attached to the word 'Son'. It appears before 'God', making it clear that there is one God – lest we mistake the evangelist for a dirty pagan. It is better translated as '*a* son of *the* God', or perhaps 'of the nature of the God', as we might figuratively use the phrase 'a son of a bitch' for someone with the nature of a dog. Emperors, for example, had long been referred to as *divi filius*.[54]

The idea of Jesus being the <u>only</u> son of God is found in *The Gospel of John*, but is entirely absent from *Matthew, Mark, Luke*, and all of the known apocryphal and gnostic texts. It is also absent from the oldest surviving manuscripts of *John*. Whereas in most Bibles *John* 1:34 reads 'This is the Son of God', second and third century Greek manuscripts,[55] [56] as well as some later Latin versions,[57] [58] use a different phrase: 'This is the *chosen one* of God'.[59] Nor do ancient versions of *John* feature the famous words 'only begotten son'. This phrase was also absent from the original Nicene Creed of 325AD, and became official church dogma only with the Creed of 381AD. This nasty work of political strategy, sanctified as liturgy by the papacy, is the final word on many matters of Catholic orthodoxy.[60]

Long before popes and pontiffs began their meddling, however, the ambiguous trickster character had begun to split down the middle. One pivotal figure in the sequence of deities is Dionysus, who was born in a stable, performed miracles with wine, and was killed and reborn.[61] [62] [63] His worshippers ate the flesh and drank the blood of a sacrifice, which was transubstantiated into the god's own flesh before consumption.[64] He looked much as Christ is depicted in church art, with his long hair and magnificent beauty, but Dionysus also had another face. Ovid called him:

> the most beautiful sight in the depths of the morning
> and evening sky, your face like a virgin's when you
> stand before us without your horns.[65]

Here in the Eleusinian mysteries, his two sides come together under the influence of the mysterious beverage *kykeon* (more about that in *Neuro-Apocalypse*). Generally, however, the faces of dawn and dusk, leading us into darkness and light, were separate but close. Dionysus was always accompanied by Pan, his servant and friend, but in Christendom Pan's horns, hooves and appetites were assumed by the dark side.

The New Testament does not force this dichotomy upon us; in fact, Jesus' meeting with the devil echoes Jacob's battle with God, and leaves him something greater than he was. The devil approaches him with three temptations immediately after his baptism, when he is walking alone. He passes the tests, and before the end of the chapter his ministry has begun, and 'the people which sat in darkness saw great light'.[66] Here the devil is our old friend the light bringer, passing to the Nazarene the power to bring light.

Elsewhere Jesus is a fire-bringer, and speaks with some pride about it:

> I am come to send fire on the earth; and what will I if it
> be already kindled?[67]

131

In pagan folklore, when a woman is impregnated by a spirit, the child is born a hero, a monster, or a trickster. In Christian legend, if the woman is Mary, the father is God and the child is born the Christ. If it is any woman other than Mary, however, the father is an incubus and the child is a demon. This is not the only point where there is a correspondance between the saviour and the demonic realms. Jesus is the Son of God, who descends to earth to suffer, and Lucifer is God's favourite angel, who descends into a pit of suffering.

There is also a yeasty enigma. The Feast of Passover, when Jesus became sacrifice incarnate, is when Jews sacrifice yeast from their bread, and eat *matzah* unleavened. Leaven usually symbolises the devil and everything bad in *The New Testament*,[68] [69] but it also refers to the Kingdom of Heaven.[70] Finally, on the last page of *The New Testament*, Jesus makes a candid curtain call, calling himself the 'bright and morning star'.[71] This recalls *Isaiah*'s 'how art thou fallen from heaven, O shining one, son of the morning!'[72] 'Shining one' is *cheyel*, translated into Latin as Lucifer. In Hebrew it refers to the Babylonian god of the Morning Star – which is Venus, the planet which reflects the light of the sun before dawn.

Christ and Lucifer are not the same, of course; they are as different as heads and tails, the two sides of a coin. Their relationship is as close and complex as the relationship between good and bad. Church fathers, however, preferred to keep it simple (and besides, the horned and horny one was far more useful as a bogeyman scaring the bejeezebub out of people). The fertile ambiguity of the early Christian spectrum was rendered in black and white, and Satan became a convenient repository for everything awful. St. Justin, for example, with prodigious circularity to challenge the very Ouroboros himself, invoked devils to explain away the many similarities between the Saviour and pagan gods.[72] He described how devils had heard the prophesies about Christ and spread false signs before his arrival: the murder and resurrection of Bacchus; the virgin birth of Perseus; the healing touch of Asclepius; and the rites of Mithras. 'Those who believe these things we pity,' he wrote magnanimously, 'and those who invented them we know to be devils.'[73]

Despite Christ's two key rules being non-dualistic, Pauline dualism took hold all the same, and held fast. The cursed dichotomy between truth and the lie also manifested in another manner, which Alan Watts calls 'the tragedy of Christian history'.[74] Whereas the ancients considered myths as timeless truths expressed in the cycles of nature, the church fixed the story in historical time, and the Creed made Jesus' resurrection _in the flesh_ a dogma to be accepted, on pain of eternal pain. A tragically authoritarian and moralistic religion grew like a cancer within the Christian world from of a lively story of rebellion and ambiguity.

The figure at the boundary carries conflicting currents into our world, causing havoc as he reveals the hidden. He is the engine of history, drawing good and evil, pain and progress from behind the veil into the world, always in balance, these gifts of the light-bringer. Life and death chase one another round the circle and up the spiral, prey pursued by the claws of death and predators in hot pursuit, fleeing the abyss of hunger. Life grows wiser, faster and more refined, leaving slower genes and empires behind in a race across the aeons, wiggly-waggly-Hegely Marx carved through history. The conical spiral is the form of the _akotô_ shell sacred to Exu,[75] describing his movements in our world, leading us higher through inscrutable circuits.

A knife cuts both ways, chopping firewood and slitting throats. A Tesla coil is neither good nor bad in itself, but the first to fully exploit its potential in radio was Hitler, beaming his fiery rhetoric to millions of German speakers. Pioneers stretch beyond the limits of the actual into the potential, innovating, exploring, exploiting and corrupting as they extend empires, leaving tools floating in their wake. As the Romans decimated tribal cultures, they dispersed the letters for a worldwide scrabble game. The English tongue rolled out from behind stiff upper lips and the killer teeth of the Empire, issuing orders over territory on which the sun never set, but when this new thing it named India was organised enough for Gandhi to marshal an orderly resistance movement, the serpent bit its own tail. The trickster switched sides and broke the Raj. His latest and greatest information coup is the internet – the child of a Pentagon project called ARPANET, promising freedom and control in equally apocalyptic measure.[76] Thanks to a string of rapacious imperialists, we can e-mail almost anywhere in Roman letters, and search through practically the entire knowledge pool of the species. Empires arise and fall, but the messenger remains victorious.

The trickster enlightens wherever he strikes, in Bible stories, Yoruba legends, Native American tales and Greek myths. Both Coyote and Prometheus steal fire from the gods and give it to man. Lucifer the light bringer makes Christ shine, but he was demonised by the church. It might be a tautology to note that *daemons* were demonised by the Church, transformed rather uncharitably from neutral supernatural entities into outright malevolent nasties of the nether regions. Lucifer himself is of a different order entirely.

Loki's name also recalls fire (*logi* in Old Norse), and he is another tricky fellow, who crosses boundaries so far as to become pregnant. Malicious and quick, he steals Thor's wife's hair as she sleeps, and then schemes to get himself out of trouble. He contracts the dwarves to smithy a fine wig for her, but also exploits a rivalry to win other prizes – including Thor's Hammer, the only weapon which can kill the giants.

Like a sulphurous scientist, Loki plays his initial trick simply because he can, to get one up on a rival. Repairing the damage, he discovers useful tools, much as our own Promethean enquiry leads to solutions, either water filters and flood breaks to alleviate damage already done, or chance discoveries down unrelated avenues of research. Loki's son, the Fenris Wolf, bites off the hand of the god of single combat and glory, recalling how weapons born of science (drones, for example) take the skill and glory from battle. Loki also sired the Midgard Serpent, which stretches around the world to bite his own tail. This symbol is the ouroboros, a glyph found in many cultures, representing, at one level, self-reflexivity. Loki is bound by his son's entrails in a self-reflexive image, and tortured between heaven and earth; he is also caught in a net that he himself made. Tricksters tend to be caught by their own handiwork. Coyote falls in the dust while admiring his beautiful coat, and also falls into a giant pile of his own shit after curiously tasting a laxative herb.[77] Similarly reflexive, Rumpelstiltskin is caught when he reveals his own name, and in his fury he stamps the ground so hard that he makes a hole, which he then falls into.

Loki's final appearance is at Ragnarok, where the half-god of chaos fights Heimdall, the guardian of Asgard and of order. Both are annihilated at the twilight of the gods, and the world is destroyed and reborn. The image of two opposites against each other is common with the trickster, and reminiscent of the two snakes winding around the staff of the Greek trickster Hermes. The battle may be fought between two characters, like Loki and Heimdall or Christ and the devil, or within one character, with the self-reflexive trick or the snake biting his tail. As Jung notes of the trickster archetype, 'his body is not a unity, and his two hands fight each other.'[78]

Foolish man with your Euclidian lines of enquiry, you lower your head to charge and don't look up until you hit a wall! You imagine the direction of movement is the bearing of travel, but life curves. Chinese ghosts move in dead straight lines, but dragons undulate in living rhythms. Step back and see the snakes sliding like a corkscrew the same way, lubricated lasciviously, rubbing and writhing, wrestling and rooting in a clinch of love and hate as they twist out of the crack between the worlds, black and white and red all over. Archangels and Satan both serve God, Darth Vader is Luke's father, and the force is strong in both. If we are partisan, it is because we have half-forgotten our myths, and started watching at Episode IV.

In our neatly divided fields, bishops of Scientism and architects of the Law lay down limits to bind us; but the snake grows by tearing through its own dead skin, and kills with a single bite. Poisonous fruits grow within fences, keeping the unknown out and the inquisitive in, while CCTV and intelligent circuits observe our infractions; but there is a crooked old *orixa* at the border. He slips sweetly through gaps in defences, doffing his multicoloured hat with a sinister smile, carrying cards from unthinkable places. His messages are buried in punchlines, coded in the babblings of fools and heretics, locked in the alkaloids of power plants. They are whispered from beyond the fence to prisoners pushing against it, for Exu has boundary issues. He disturbs the peace and questions assumptions. His truths are half-lies, his manners are dreadful, and he can't be trusted any more than you can. But leave his alarm unchecked and he'll emerge on your skin as an ominous rash, or burn in your heart as a coal of anger. He'll jump you on a moody street at twilight, or smash through the fence in a hijacked plane if he has to, but he will be heard, because only through him can the father can be reached and the whole be known. Pay attention, sons and daughters of mortals and gods, because his glitches are our salvation.

Layure Exu!

Tao
gives birth
to one

A
snake
seeking
its
tail
traces
a
single
point
going
round
a
circle;
source
of
a
sine
wave

One
gives birth
to Two

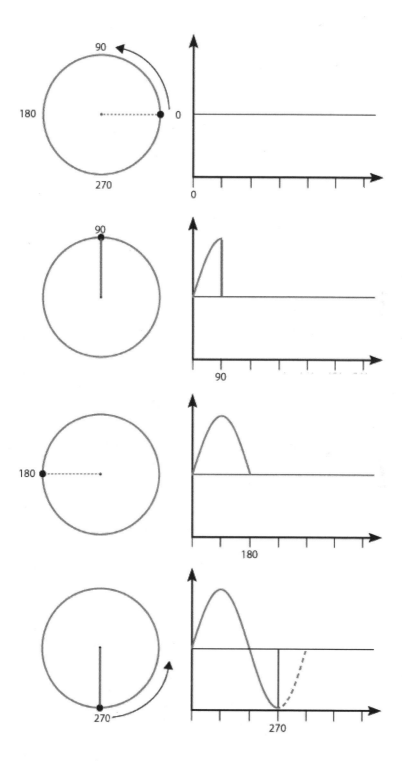

positive,

rises   *then*

wave   *drops*

sine   *down*

The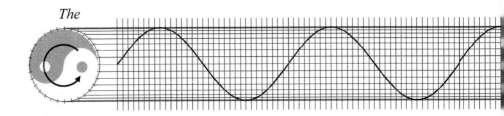

negative,

a

vanishing

tang

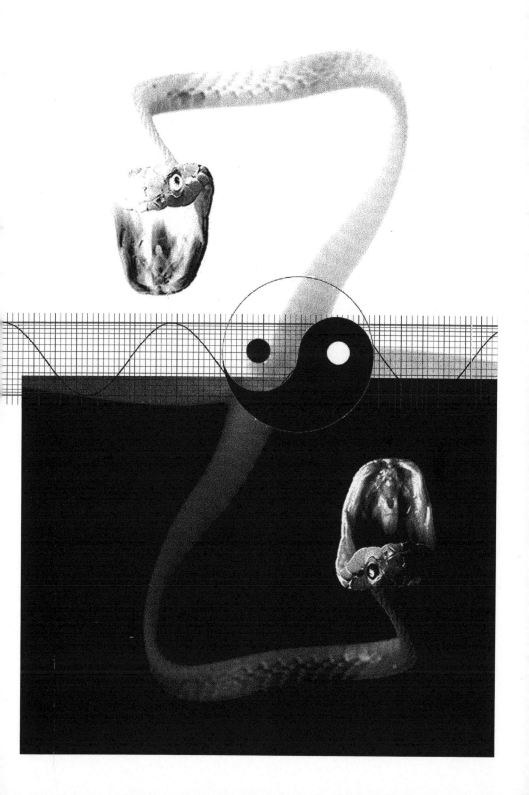

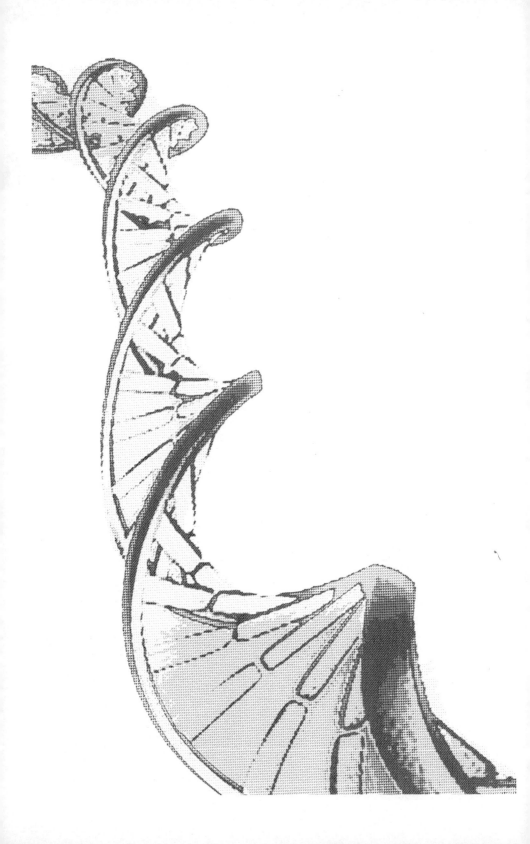

next,

    into   *past*

  now   *condensed*

  drawing   *and*

difference   *pulled*

of   *through*

point   *into*

a   *the*

ent,   *pres*

T h e
sine winds through
the centre of the yin-yang,
expanding along polarities in all
dimensions, in the rhythm of the breath
and the wash of the tides. Here are the shapes
of life, the sigma curve of organic growth
and the normal distribution of a population.

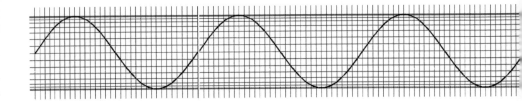

One point in a zero sum-game, two players
equal and opposite, where all opposites
are unities; up and down, form and
space, good and evil; sense and anti-
sense depend on which strand
you stand, on how you
understand.

Heads surge ahead, tails tracing twists of
history behind. Life is not sentimental, and
the sage in is not sentimental. Exquisitely
balanced upon the snakes, and with
fantastically bendy kung fu legs, he
is ready for any twist.

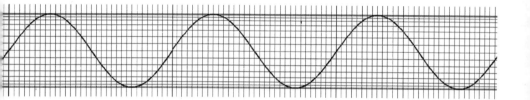

Dark
and light spill into
our plane of awareness, one
stream with two currents. One flows as
the other goes, growth shifts into contraction,
two sides of a fraction, rising together around
each other, plunging into downward spirals.

Two give

birth   to   three

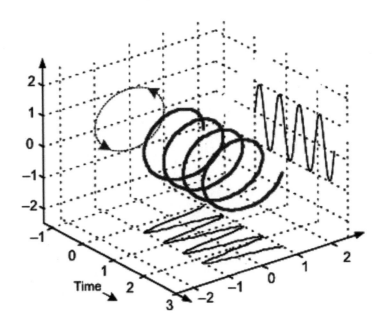

In cross-section, the threads of a double helix point in opposite directions; but they spiral the same way.

Creation and destruction are in the forming and breaking of bonds, and the flow between the poles is the history of the universe. Eggs smashed in a pan, cooked in entropy into a low energy Om-lattice. Teeth and enzymes smash it up again, bind it into a body. Because we prefer sunny-side up to turd and dandruff, we make distinctions, but the dance encompasses all.

"O Arjuna, I am the Supreme Spirit abiding in the inner psyche of all beings.

I am also the creator, maintainer, and destroyer - or the beginning, the middle, and the end - of all beings."[79]

Bhagavad Gita

A trail
passes through
the plane of
awareness

later
elsewehere, the
same signature in a
different form, arising
and shrinking
away

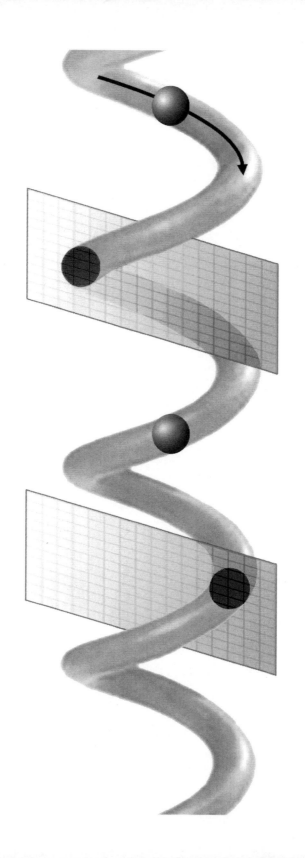

Trails

circle

hidden

through

dark

dimensions

emerging
briefly into
the light of
mind

Coils
    of
    code
        wind
            wide
                and
                    divide,
                        th ey
                    split   chafe
                into   and
                sides   collide,
                    and   they

            hybridise

Three

give birth to

all universal

things

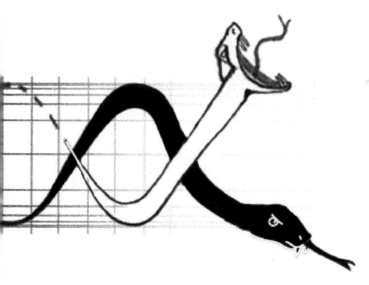

A
tail and
two heads, but
when it bites, it
is one or the
other.

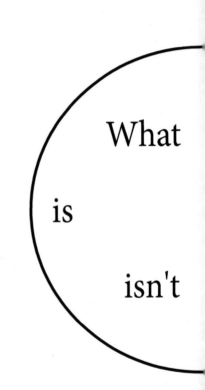

half

half

also

If
the wave
packet collapses
over this
side

Then
the packet
can't collapse
over this
side

$$1 + \text{-}1 = 0$$

$$2 = 0$$

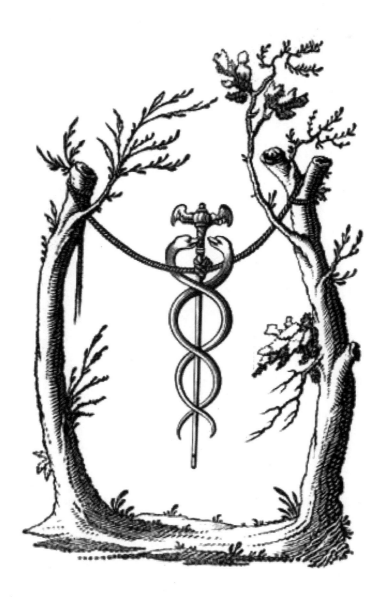

POST-SCRIPT

To Bennett

'Never compose anything unless the not composing of it becomes a positive nuisance to you.'

Gustav Holst[1]

Kyoto, 2002

I think I am writing a book. I'm not sure about this, but I believe I am writing a book, though I don't feel fully in control of the situation – more like I am watching a book being written. Of course, I am not channelling like those weirdoes my granny used to climb holy mountains with. No madam, this work is mine, though the *me* of 'mine' is different to the *me* with which I am familiar. That *me* certainly has a poor command of grammar, and writes serpentine tracts punctuated at will and wriggling with digressions. Anyway, I never set out to write a book, I wanted to be a fireman. One of my friends periodically bullies me into editing my scrawls. Blame Bennett, and don't blame me.

This has been going on for a few years now, irregularly, but with a discernable pattern, and a subtle strategy. I have always been an insomniac, which I now suspect is part of the conspiracy of *me* against *me*. For years, as an insomniac school teacher getting up at a dreadful time in the morning, I experimented with soporific teas, exercise regimes and relaxation techniques, to no avail. Now I work privately, and my jobs tend to start at midday, which suits me (and *me*) very well. I can sit up all night, computer before me and wife softly snoring behind, bong at my left hand and peanuts at my right, and if I choose to phone home at 4am, my friends in England are just getting home from their day jobs.

Some nights, when I can't sleep, I potter around, reading, surfing the net, doing nothing constructive, and then suddenly I notice something glaring and urgent about the world, and I need to write it down. I call it a secret, but 'secret' is just a name which stuck (aren't all names just names which stuck?). I write as I think, with anarchic grammar, half-page sentences illustrated with ugly scrawls and pictures of sine waves. The secrets don't take very long, usually twenty minutes or so, and as the subject winds around to a conclusion, I become very sleepy indeed. This is quite out of character. Sleeping is usually a matter of will for me, not because I am tired, but because I really should go to sleep and I have run out of peanuts.

In the morning, I find one of three things. It may be an angry rant, about the police perhaps, without much depth to it, the residue from some form of therapeutic eruption. Other times I am left with a laboriously explored platitude: 'the universe is' or something; again there is not much to be done with it. Other times I have something workable between the extremes. I never select a subject, but it is nearly always some aspect of the Tao, the abstract world, something about non-action or awareness, or the end of time.

The secrets don't just come at night, but they rarely come without a bong. My entire corpus is a stoned corpus. Secrets come into mind and melt away if I don't write them down, so they have been scrawled on napkins and the backs of envelopes, on students' homework and punched into my mobile phone. Tucking into lunch at my boss' house, an entire secret may pass before the green tea is served and I can run for a pen without being rude. They come at ridiculous times. I scrawled one at a wedding reception in Tokyo. I wrote a kabbalistic analysis of *2001: A Space Odyssey* while having sex (she didn't seem to mind, but the writing went a bit wobbly around *Binah*). I have moonlighted sitting in the office, writing reams about Napoleon while my co-workers do data entry.

If I smoke too often, the secrets stop coming, which doesn't bother me, but it does tally with traditional Shaiva and Rasta prescriptions reserving herbs for spiritual and artistic purposes. Perhaps one day I will develop some self-restraint, who knows? Another confession is that this whole creative (or therapeutic) period of my life began when I stopped meditating. I struggled daily for five years until coming across Alan Watts's description of obsessive meditation as 'aching legs Zen', and gave up that very instant. My tired dedication was just a habit, and not a habit I was enjoying.

Now I meditate when the mood takes me, and it is almost hedonistic when I do. I also watch myself write rather than make myself write. The scrappy secrets go into an envelope, and some of them get cleaned up later and typed into my computer as a second draft, which is still unreadable. This job takes care of my less inspired insomniac moments. A few times a year, when Bennett's website goes out, I look through the second drafts and work them into readable articles. This job is testing, something like tying spaghetti together, but I have been surprised to find a semblance of order, a number of interrelated themes, and some kind of an argument. I have no idea why one theme (for example 'processes rather than objects') should be mixed with unrelated ideas and spread across three secrets, making it necessary to splice about like an endonuclease trying to tease sense from nonsense.

There is the metaphor I was looking for – the obscure *me*, the source of the ideas is the DNA. Bennett is a hormone demanding expression, the secrets are the messenger RNA emerging from the dark and tangled nucleus; leaving me, this me, as the ribosome, splicing, translating, and arranging. Let's hope we can whip up some viable proteins.

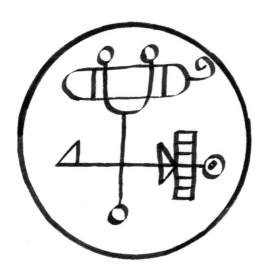

Bibliographical notes

To Rob Psypress

PREFACE: MESSIAH APPREHENDED AT HEATHROW!

1. *Jerusalem Syndrome* - Yair Bar-El et al. in *The British Journal of Psychiatry* (2000) 176: pp. 86-90
2. *Psilocybin-Induced Contraction of Nearby Visual Space* - Roland Fischer et al. *Agents and Actions* 1, no. 4 (1970), pp. 190-197
3. *Pahnke's "Good Friday Experiment': a long-term follow-up and methodological critique* - Doblin, R. in *Journal of Transpersonal Psychology*, 1991: 23(1)
4. *Chemical analysis of residues from seventeenth century clay pipes from Stratford-upon-Avon and environs* - Thackeray, J. F. et al in *South African Journal of Science* 97: pp 19-21
5. *Song of Solomon* 5:11-16

1) The Blunt Edge of Ockham's Razor

1. *Summa Totius Logicae* - William of Ockham i. 12
2. *A Dictionary of Philosophy* - Flew, A (London: 1979) p. 253
3. *Handbook to Life in the Medieval World* - Cosman, M. P. et al (New York: 2008) p. 356
4. *The Mathematical Principles of Natural Philosophy* - Newton (A. Motte trans.) (London, 1729)
5. Ibid.
6. *Wild Talents* - Charles Fort, chap. 22.
7. From the National Abortion Federation website
8. *Letters of the Abbey of Saint-Joseph de Clairval*, March 1st, 1999
9. *The Gay Science*, Book III - Nietzche, F, p. 108
10. Cooper p. 65
11. *The Tibetan Book of the Dead* - (Chogyam Trungpa trans.)
12. *Kalama Sutta* - (Soma Thera trans.) (Kandy: Buddhist Publication Society, 1981)
13. *The Forge and the Crucible: The Origins and Structures of Alchemy* - Mircea Eliade (Stephen Corrin trans.) (Chicago, 1978) p.231
14. *The Mathematical Principles of Natural Philosophy* - Isaac Newton (London, 1729) (Motte, A. trans.)

2) Killer creeds and dirty deeds

1. *The Lion and the Unicorn: Socialism and the English Genius* in *Why I Write* - George Orwell (Penguin 2004) p. 11
2. *Howard Zinn on History* - Zinn, H p. 99
3. Ibid. p. 110
4. *America* - Alistair Cooke (Random House, 1973)
5. *The American Indian in Western Legal Thought: The Discourses of Conquest* - Robert A. Williams (New York, 1990), p. 211 (quoting Governor Harvey)
6. Cooke, p. 36
7. Zinn p. 99
8. Cooke, p. 37
9. *Pocahontas and her world: a chronicle of America's first settlement in which is related the story of the Indians and the Englishmen, particularly Captain John Smith* - Captain Samuel
10. *Declaration of Independence* - Washington, G. Franklin B. et al
11. Ibid.
12. Cooke, p. 37
13. *The Choctaws in Oklahoma: From Tribe to Nation, 1855-1970* - Clara Sue Kidwell, Lindsay G. Robertson (Oklahoma, 2007) p. 137
14. *A Western Hemisphere Perspective on the History of Violence* - Phillip L. Walker & Richard H. Steckel (71st Annual Meeting of the American Association of Physical Anthropologists
15. *Capitalism, Socialism and Democracy* - Joseph A. Schumpeter, chapter 13
16. Master Sheng Yen's Dharma Talk (October 24, 1993) http://www.dharmadrumretreat.org

3) The Hidden Genius of Science

1. *Kekulé memorial lecture* - Japp, F.R. 1898. *Journal of the Chemical Society*, 73, pp. 97-138
2. *The Complete Patents of Nikola Tesla Glenn*, J. (ed.) (New York, 1994) chapter 4
3. *My Inventions: The Autobiography of Nikola Tesla* - Tesla, N. (Filiquarian Publishing, 2006) p. 11
4. *America's forgotten innovator, Nikola Tesla* - Mast, A. (Florida State University). pp. 14–15

5. *The Varieties of Religious Experience* - William James (Electronic
Classics Series) p. 25
6. *The Foundations of Science: Science and Hypothesis, The Value
of Science, Science and Method* - Henri Poincaré & George Bruce
Halsted (Science Press, 1946) p. 390
7. *Kekulé memorial lecture* - Japp, F.R. 1898. *Journal of the
Chemical Society*, 73, pp. 97-138
8. Ibid.
9. *An Autobiographic Sketch* - Loewi O. in *Perspectives in Biology
and Medicine*, Vol IV,1, Autumn 1960:17
10. *Einstein: A Life* - Denis Brian (New York, 1995) pp. 60-61
11. *Islands of Truth: A Mathematical Mystery Cruise* - Peterson, I.
(New York, 1990) pp. 171-178
12. *Less Proof, More Truth* - Chaitin, G. in New Scientist 107 July
28th 2007
13. *Dream Interpretation as a Psychotherapeutic Technique* -
Coolidge, F. L. (Abingdon: 2006) p.39
14. *Letters of Wolfgang Amadeus Mozart* - Hans Mersmann, ed. (M.
M. Bozman trans.) (London, 1928) preface pp. vii-viii
15. *Devotions from the World of Music* - Barbara Kavanaugh (David
C. Cook, 2000)
16. *Letter to Thomas Butts, 25th April, 1803*, in *Complete Writings:
with Variant Readings* - William Blake, (Keynes. G. ed.) (Oxford,
1969) pp. 822-823
17. *Thus Spake Zarathustra* - Nietzsche, F. (Thomas Common
trans.) quote from the introduction by his sister.
18. Quoted in *The Eureka! Moment: 100 Key Scientific Discoveries
of the 20th Century* - Lee, R. (Routledge, 2002) p. 95
19. *Freud's Philosophy of the Unconscious* - Smith, D. L. (Springer,
1999) p. 68
20. *Invention and the Unconscious* - Joseph Marie Montmasson,
(Henry Hatfield trans.) (Routledge, 1932) p. 76
21. *Artificial Intelligence and Symbolic Computation*: International
Conference AISC 2000, Madrid, Spain, July 17-19, 2000, *Revised
Papers* - J. A. Campbell, Eugenio Roanes-Lozano (Springer, 2001) p. 7
22. *Autohypnotic Experiences of Milton H. Erickson* - Erickson, M.
H. & Rossi, E. L. in *The American Journal of Clinical Hypnosis*,
July. 1977 20, pp. 36-54
23. *The Heretic in Darwin's court: the life of Alfred Russel Wallace*

Ross - Slotten, A. (New York. 2004) pp. 144-14

24. *Everything's Relative* - Tony Rothman (Wiley, 2003) p. 144

25. *Quoted in My Life and Loves* - Harris, F. & Gallagher, J. F. (Grove Press, 1991) p. 594

26. *Divine Love and Wisdom* - Swedenborg, verse 391

27. *True Christian Religion* - Swedenborg, verse 60

28. *De Infinito* - Swedenborg, verse 143

29. *Dhamma Texts* - Sayagyi U Ba Khin. Available online at http://www.ubakhin.com

30. *The Atmosphere of Heaven The Unnatural Experiments of Dr Beddoes and His Sons of Genius* - Jay, M (2010)

31. *On some Hegelisms* - William James. (1882) *Mind* 7: 186-208

32. *Mescal: A New Artificial Paradise* - Ellis, H. in *The Contemporary Review* January 1898

33. *Technology for the Prevention of "Les Maladies Produites par la Masturbation'* - Bullough, V. L. in *Technology and Culture*, Vol. 28, No. 4, October, 1987, pp. 828-832

34. *Psilocybin-Induced Contraction of Nearby Visual Space* - Roland Fischer et al. *Agents and Actions* 1, no. 4 (1970), pp. 190-197

35. *Pass It On: The Story of Bill Wilson and How the A. A. Message Reached the World* (Alcoholics Anonymous 1984)

36. *Ketamine-assisted psychotherapy (KPT) of heroin addiction: immediate effects and six months follow-up* - Krupitsky, E.M. et al. *MAPS Bulletin* 9(4), (1999-2000) pp. 21-26.

37. *Ketamine psychedelic therapy (KPT): a review of the results of ten years of research* - Krupitsky, E.M. & Grinenko A.Y. *Journal of Psychoactive Drugs* 29(2) (1997) pp. 165-183.

38. *New Hope for Alcoholics* - Hoffer, A. and Osmond, H. (1968). New Hyde Park, NY: University Books.

39. *Sigmund Freud's Cocaine Years* - Nuland, S. *The New York Times Sunday Book Review* 21 July 2011

40. *LSD: My Problem Child* - Albert Hofmann (McGraw-Hill, 1980) p. 12

41. *Food of the Gods* - Terrence McKenna chap. 14

42. *The effects of LSD-25 on creativity and tolerance to regression* - Zegans, L. S. et al. in *Archives of General Psychiatry*, 1967;16: pp. 740-749

43. *Psychedelic Agents in Creative Problem-Solving: A Pilot Study* -

Harman, W. W. et al, *Psychological Reports*, 19:211-227, 1966.
44. *LSD: The Geek's Wonder Drug* - Ann Harrison January 1st, 2006, *Wired Magazine Online*
45. *The Scientific Search for the Soul: Part I* with Francis Crick, Ph.D. in *Thinking Allowed* (Thinking Allowed Productions)
46. *The Times*, July 24th, 1967
47. *Foucault, in Postmodernism: Critical Concepts* - Victor E. Taylor, Charles E. Winquist (Taylor & Francis, 1998) p. 331
48. *Psychedelics and the Creation of Virtual Reality in MAPS (Multidisciplinary Association for Psychedelic Studies)* vol. X, no. 3, *Creativity* 2000
49. *The Tao of Physics: An Exploration of the Parallels Between Modern Physics and Eastern Mysticism* - Capra, F (Berkeley: 2000) 4th ed. p. 12
50. *Daily Telegraph*, May 21st, 2005
51. *The Man Who Loved Only Numbers: The Story of Paul Erdös and the Search for Mathematical Truth* - Hoffman, P.
52. *MAPS Bulletin*, vol. X, no. 3, p. 23
53. *Human Personality and Its Survival of Bodily Death* - Frederic W. H. Myers (Kessinger Publishing: 2003) p. 91
54. *Forty Years of On The Road 1957-1997* - Gyenis, A. (1997) in *DHARMA Beat* Issue 9
55. *"Ken Kesey." Critical Survey of Long Fiction* - Reilly, E. C. (2000): EBSCO. Web. 2010.
56. *Chemical analysis of residues from seventeenth century clay pipes from Stratford-upon-Avon and environs* - Thackeray, J. F. et al in *South African Journal of Science* 97: pp 19-21
57. *A cannabis reader: global issues and local experiences. Perspectives on cannabis controversies, treatment and regulation in Europe* - Sharon Rödner Sznitman, et al. (EMCDDA Monographs) p. 6
58. *The Total Library: Non-fiction 1922* - 1986 Borges, J. L. (Penguin, 2001) pp. 370-371
59. *Mysterium Cosmographicum* - Kepler, J. (1596)
60. *The Devil's Doctor* - Philip Ball p. 251
61. *Paracelsus: The Mercurial Mage* - David Hambling in *The Fortean Times* April 2002
62. Ball, P. p. 239
63. *Alchemy* - Eric John Holmyard (Dover 1990), p. 170

64. Ball, P. p. 357

65. *Newton, the Man* - Keynes, J. M. (from Columbia University in the City of New York, Department of Physics website)

66. *Opticks* - Newton, I. (1704)

67. *Newton to Oldenburg*, April 26, 1676, quoted by Principe, L. M. in *Rethinking the Scientific Revolution* (Cambridge: 2000) - Osler M. J. (ed) p. 208

68. Ball, p. 331

69. Ball, p. 281

70. *The Western Medical Tradition 800BC - AD 1800* - Lawrence I. Conrad et al. (New York, 1995) p. 312

71. *Arcana Cœlestia* - Swedenborg, verses 128-129

72. *Isaac Newton's Freemasonry: The Alchemy of Science and Mysticism* - Alain Bauer (Inner Traditions, 2007), chap. 3

73. Ball p. 163

74. *My View of the World* - Schrodinger, E. (Cambridge 2000)

75. *God Is Not One* - Prothero, S. (2010), S. p. 144

76. *On Miracles and Modern Spiritualism* - Wallace, A. R. (Cambridge: 2009)

77. *The History of Spiritualism* - Sir Arthur Conan Doyle Volume II, Chapter 3

78. Wallace, A. R. p. 82

79. Ibid. p. 103

80. *Obsessive Genius: The inner world of Marie Curie* - Barbara Goldsmith (W.W. Norton, 2005), p. 138

81. *Ideas and Opinions* - Einstein, A (New York: 1950) pp.41 - 49

82. *Disturbing Times: The State of the Planet and Its Possible Future* - Scott Firsing (30° South Publishers, 2007) p. 142

83. Question posted by Stephen Hawking on Yahoo Answers

84. Ibid.

85. *Atomic Education Urged by Einstein* in *New York Times* May, 25, 1946

4) The Politics of Truth

1. *The Autocrat of the Breakfast Table* - Holmes, O. W. Sr. (1858) Boston: *The Atlantic Monthly.*

2. *Novum Organum* - Bacon, F. (1620)

3. *The Contagiousness of Puerperal Fever* - Holmes, O. W. 1843 (Harvard Classics 1909-14)

4. *Ignaz Philipp Semmelweis, the Prophet of Bacteriology* - Hanninen O, et al in Infect Control. 1983 Sep-Oct;4(5):367-70

5. *Human Basophil Degranulation Triggered by Very Dilute Antiserum Against IgE* - Benveniste, J. et al. *Nature* 1988; 333:816-7.

6. Ibid.

7. *The Memory of Water* - Schiff, M. (San Francisco, 1995) p. 79

8. Ibid., p. 79

9. *The Guardian* 15th March, 2001

10. Schiff, M.

11. *Scientific Controversy as Farce: The Benveniste-Maddox Counter Trials* - Caroline Joan S. Picart in *Social Studies of Science,* Vol. 24, No. 1 (Feb., 1994), pp. 7-37

12. *Fear, Faith, Fact, Fantasy* - John A. Henderson (Parkway, 2003) p. 165

13. *Transatlantic Transfer of Digitized Antigen Signal by Telephone Link* - Benveniste, J., and Jurgens, P. in *Journal of Allergy and Clinical Immunology,* 1997; 99: S157

14. Schiff p. 68

15. *Letter from the General Director of INSERM to Benveniste,* in Schiff, M. p. 142

16. Transactions of the Homoeopathic Medical Society of the State of New York, 1867 p. 125

17. http://www.rsm.ac.uk/welcom/history.htm

18. *Table-Rappers: The Victorians and the Occult* - Ronald Pearsall (Sutton, 2004) p. 18

19. *Numerous Cases of Surgical Operations without Pain in the Mesmeric state* - Bailliere, H. (London: 1843)

20. *Mesmerism in India, and its Practical Application in Surgery and Medicine* - Esdaile, J. 1846/1977

21. *Mesmerized: Powers of Mind in Victorian Britain* - Alison Winter (Chicago, 2000) p. 42

22. *Etheral epidemic mesmerism and the introduction of inhalation*

anaesthesia to early Victorian London - Winter, A. in *Social History of Medicine*, vol. 4 (1991), pp. 1-27

23. *Mortality Associated with Anesthesia* - Rosenberg, H., Thomas Jefferson University

24. *Medical Nemesis* - Illich, I. (London, 1975) p. 33

25. *Incidence of Adverse Drug Reactions in Hospitalized Patients* - Lazarou J, et al. in *Journal of the American Medical Association* 1998;279:1200

26. Illich, p. 14

27. *Medical Essays* - Holmes, O. W. (Boston, 1883)

28. *The Gospel of Thomas* (Stephen Patterson & Maryin Meyer trans.), verse 6

29. *Modulating AngioGenesis: the Yin and the Yang in Ginseng* - Sengupta, S. et al. in *Circulation* 2004;110: pp. 1219-1225

30. *Phytopharmaceuticals in Cancer Chemoprevention* - Bagchi, D. & Preuss, H. (Boca Raton, 2005) pp. 349-426

31. *Influence of Piperine on the Pharmacokinetics of Curcumin in Animals and Human Volunteers* - Shoba, G. et al., May, 1998 *Planta Medica* 64 (4): pp. 353-6.

32. *Adverse drug reactions as cause of admission to hospital: prospective analysis of 18,820 patients* - Pirmohamed, M et al, BMJ Vol. 329, 3 July 2004

33. *Adverse cardiovascular and central nervous system events associated with dietary supplements containing ephedra alkaloids* - Haller, C. & Benowitz, N. New England Journal of Medicine (2000) 343 (25): pp. 1833-8

34. Marvin Lipman, quoted in *New Scientist*, 12 August, 2006 p. 12

35. Ibid.

36. *QuickStats: Percentage of All Live Births by Cesarean Delivery* - National Vital Statistics System, United States, 2005

37. Data from the American Society for Aesthetic Plastic Surgery - http://www.surgery.org/press/procedurefacts-asqf.php

38. *Excess mortality from suicide and other external causes of death among women with cosmetic breast implants* - Lipworth, L. et al in *Annals of Plastic Surgery*, 59 (2), August 2007, pp. 119-123

39. *Biologic Effects and Health Hazards of Microwave Radiation. Proceedings of an International Symposium* - Czerski, P. et al., eds. Warsaw, 15-18 Oct. 1973, pp. 289-293

40. *Electromagnetic effects – From cell biology to medicine* Richard, H.W. Funk Progress in *Histochemistry and Cytochemistry* 43 (2009) 177–264
41. *An Interview with Robert O. Becker, M. D.* - Howe, L. M. (2000)
42. Schiff, M. p. 82

5) Law, Disorder and the Question of Evil

1. *Thus Spake Zarathustra* - Nietzsche, F. chapter. 11
2. *Woman – or Suffragette?* Oxford University Press Blog - 9 April 2013 http://blog.oup.com/2013/04/suffragette-word-origin-evolution-etymology/
3. *Phaedrus* - Plato (Athens 360BC)
4. *Hagakure, The Book of the Samurai* - Tsunetomo,Y. (William Scott Wilson, trans) (New York and Tokyo 1979), p. 58
5. *The Confusions of Pleasure: Commerce and Culture in Ming China* - Timothy Brook (California: 1999) p. 230
6. *Homoeroticism in Classical Arabic Literature* - James T. Monroe, p. 117
7. Seen at an Exhibition at the British Library
8. *Naked Lunch* - Burroughs, W. p. 111
9. www.norml.org
10. *Our Kids on Ritalin* - Johnson, P., Colorado State Board of Education, 2nd Congressional District (accessed on Sept 1 2013 http://www.angelfire.com/co2/RayThomas/ritalin2.html
11. www.1800petmeds.com
12. *Drug harms in the UK: a multicriteria decision analysis* - Nutt, D. J., *The Lancet* Vol. 376, Issue 9752, 6–12 November 2010, pp. 1558–1565
13. *Police Reform and Social Responsibility Act*, provision 152
14. *Remembrances of LSD Therapy Past* Grover Eisner, B.
15. *LSD - A Dangerous Drug* in *The New England Journal of Medicine*, December 2nd, 1965
16. *Acid Dreams: The Complete Social History of LSD: The CIA, The Sixties, and Beyond* - Martin A. Lee & Bruce Shlain (Grove Press 1985) p. 38
17. *Whatever Happened To... Mind Control?* - Ornes, S. *Discover Magazine* (August 2008)
18. *What Did the C.I.A. Do to Eric Olson's Father?* - Ignatieff, M

New York Times Magazine (April 1 2001)

19. *Cocaine Politics: Drugs, Armies, and the CIA in Central America* - Scott. P. D. & Marshall, J (Berkeley: 1991), pp. x-xi.

20. *$4.7 Billion Later - No change in cocaine availability* - Juan Forero. *New York Times* August 19, 2006

21. *Assessment of a Concentrated, High-Profile Police Operation: No discernable Impact on Drug Availability, Price or Purity* - David Best et al. in *The British Journal of Criminology*, 2001, 41, pp. 738-745

22. *Programme for a Medical Prescription of Narcotics: Final Report of the Research Representatives* - Uchtenhagen, A. et al.

23. *Bristol City council must support the community and reject Tesco* - Sam Allen, www.theguardian.com, 22 April 2011

24. www.countingthebodies.org

25. *BLS American Time Use Survey*, A.C. Nielsen Co. 2013

26. *1 in 100 U.S. Adults Behind Bars, New Study Says* - Liptak, A in *New York Times* 28 February 2008

27. *Isaiah* 45

28. www.chabad.org

29. Synod of Laodicea, Canon 29

30. *Vade Mecum for Confessors Concerning Some Aspects of the Morality of Conjugal Life* - Vatican's Pontifical Council for the Family, March 1, 1997

31. *Cardinal Calls Condoms 'Lesser Evil'* - CBS News, April 21st, 2006

32. *The Book of Lieh-tzu: A Classic of Tao* - (Graham, A. C. trans.) (New York: 1960)

33. *Obedience to Authority* - Milgram, S. (New York 1974)

34. *Behavioral Study of Obedience* - Milgram, S. Sengage Learning Website

35. *The Potential for Violence in Germany* - Mantell, D.M. (1971) *Journal of Social Issues* 27, pp. 101-12.

36. *The Hypnosis of Adolf Hitler* - Post, D. E. in *Journal of Forensic Sciences*, 43(6), 1998 November.

37. Milgram, S. p. 35

38. Milgram, S. p.119

39. Milgram, S. p.118

40. *The Milgram paradigm after 35 years: Some things we now know about obedience to authority* - Blass, T. *Journal of Applied*

Social Psychology (1999), Vol. 25, pp. 955-978.

41. *Obedience* - Milgram, S. Film in the Behavioural Sciences, Pennsylvania State University (1965)

42. *On 'Obedience to Authority'* - Zimbardo, P.G. in *American Psychologist* (1974) 29:566-567

43. pers. com. Biology Teacher at School!

44. *Dynamical neural representation of song syntax in Bengalese Finch: a model study* - Nishikawa, J. and Kazuo Okanoya, K. *Ornithological Science*, Vol. 5 (2006) , No. 1 July 95-103

45. *Introducing Fractal Geometry* - Lesmoir Gordon, Rood, & Edney (Victoria 2000)

46. *Fractal analysis, a new tool for the spatial analysis of urban patterns* - Frankhauser, P. in *Spatial analysis of biodemographic data* (Bocquet-Appel, J-P, et al. eds). (Montrouge: 1996) pp. 311-340

47. *Random texts exhibit Zipf's-law-like word frequency distribution* - Li, W. IEEE *Transactions on Information Theory* 38 (1992) pp. 1842-1845

48. *A real time morphology for artificial life creatures* - McDermott, P. thesis (April 2006), University of Manchester.

49. *Britain near top of Europe's teenage binge-drinking league* - Smithers, R. theguardian.com, 26 March 2009

50. *The 1947 Soviet famine and the entitlement approach to famines* - Ellman, M Cambridge Journal of Economics 2000, 24, pp. 603–630

51. *The Stanford Prison Experiment* - Zimbardo, P. G. Inc. CBS News.

52. *A Century of Change: Trends in UK statistics since 1900* - Research Paper 99/111, House of Commons Library - 21st December 1999, p. 14

53. *The Lucifer Principle* - Howard Bloom (New York 1997) pp. 258-259

54. Data analysis using the 2004 Health Organization (WHO) Mortality Statistics http://www.socsci.uci.edu/~cpb/peace/countries.htm) and the World Bank's 2002 World Development Index & http://www.infoplease.com/ipa/A0908770.html

55. *The Lion and the Unicorn: Socialism and the English Genius* - Orwell, G. (1941)

56. *Crime in South Africa Grows More Vicious* - *New York Times*,

September 23rd, 2005 & *South Africa police killings rise* - BBC
Website Wednesday, 19th July 2006
57. *Tao Te Ching*, chapter 3
58. *Confucius and the Analects: New Essays* 211 - Bryan W. Van
Norden, (NetLibrary) p. 281
59. http://www.mosuoproject.org/
60. *Robbers on Robbery: Prevention and the Offender* - Wright, R
and Decker S. H. 15 April 2002 National Criminal Justice Research
Service
61. Unabomber's Manifesto
62. *Dying to Win: The Strategic Logic of Suicide Terrorism* - Pape,
R. (London, 2006) p. 81
63. Ibid. Pape, pp. 79-101
64. *Martyr myth: Inside the minds of suicide bombers* - Adam
Lankford New Scientist website 8 July 2013
65. *Road design? He calls it a revolution* - Lyall, S. in *The Herald
Tribune*, January 22nd, 2005
66. *A Review of Global Road Accident Fatalities* - Jacobs, G. D. and
Aeron-Thomas, A. (transport for development website)
67. *Tao Te Ching*, chap. 17
68. *Tao Te Ching*, chap. 77
69. *In Mexico, an upsurge of vigilantism* - Thomson, A. *Financial
Times*, 12 April 2013
70. *No such thing as a free lunch?* - Renton, A. - *The Observer* 19
August 2007
71. *No such thing as a free lunch?* - Relph, D. BBC News 9 August
2007
72. *Resistance to Civil Government* - Thoreau, H. D. (1849)
73. Ibid.
74. *A Conversation with Michel Foucault* - Simon, J. in *Partisan
Review*, 38 (1971), pp. 192-201
75. Milgram film (1965)

6) The Monk, the Mystic and the Mosquito

1. *Deforestation and Frontier Expansion in Brazilian Amazonia* - Diogenes S. Alves (Instituto Nacional de Pesquisas Espaciais)
2. *Nepal: Development Performance and Prospects* - A World Bank Country Study, South Asia Regional Office, World Bank, Washington, (1979)
3. *The feral cane toad (Bufo marinus) Invasive species fact sheet* - Department of the Environment and Heritage, 2004
4. *Wildlife Damage Management,* from the Colorado State University website
5. *The Riddle of Lake Victoria* - Ron Coleman, in *Cichlid News Magazine* October 2001 pp. 32-34
6. *Escaped GM grass could spread bad news* - Michael Hopkin in *Nature News,* August 11th, 2006
7. Andy Coghlan, *New Scientist,* August 12, 2006 p. 9
8. *Wake Your Inner life Force* - Alexander, J. in *The Daily Mail* January 1st, 1994
9. *The Midrash on Psalms,* Vol. 2, *Psalm 34* (Braude W. G. trans.) (Yale: 1959)
10. *I Corinthians* 1:25
11. *Holy Madness* - Feuerstein, G. (Prescott, 2006), chapter 1
12. *The Divine Madman: The Sublime Life and Songs of Drukpa Kunley* (Keith Dowden trans.) (Pilgrim Press: 2000) p. 16
13. *The Little Flowers of St. Francis* - (W. Heywood trans.), (1906) P. 85
14. James, W. p. 37
15. *On Being Sane in Insane Places* - Rosenham D. L. (1973) *Science* 197 (70): pp. 250-258
16. *The Trap: What happened to our dream of freedom?* - Curtis, A. BBC 2 documentary (aired March 2007)
17. R. D. Laing, quoted in R. D. Laing, *Self, Symptom and Society* - Sedgewick, P.
18. *Diclofenac residues as the cause of vulture population decline in Pakistan* - J. Lindsay Oaks et al. *Nature,* vol. 427, February 12th 2004
19. *Bird Life International,* 2006
20. *One Quick Shot May Not be Enough* in *The Economist,* April 12th, 2008

7) From layered truths to horns and hooves: Exu's Journey

1. *The Trickster in West Africa: A Study of Mythic Irony and Sacred Delight* - Pelton, R. D. (London,
1980) p. 130
2. *Jeremiah* 27:6
3. *Genesis* 12: 14-16
4. *Genesis* 19:8
5. *Genesis* 19: 31-37
6. *Genesis* 25: 31-34
7. *Genesis* 27:21-30
8. *Genesis* 34
9. *Numbers* 31:15-18
10. *Jeremiah* 24:2
11. *Exodus* 32
12. *Leviticus* 26; 46
13. *Leviticus* 25:39 - 46
14. *Leviticus* 24:13-23
15. *Leviticus* 17: 9
16. *Isaiah* 45:7
17. *Mark* 2:18-19
18. *Mark* 2:26
19. *Mark* 2:23
20. *Luke* 9:60
21. *Mark* 21:12
22. *John* 8:7
23. *Matthew* 21:12
24. *John* 10:19
25. *Luke* 12:51 - 53
26. *Matthew* 27:46
27. *Mark* 12:29-30
28. *Mark* 12:31
29. See *I Corintians* 13:3
30. *John* 10:30
31. *The Christian Book of Why* - McCollister, J. C. (Jonathan David Publishers 1983), pp 205 - 206
32. *John* 6:35
33. *Luke* 2:8
34. *The Two Babylons: Or The Papal Worship Proved to Be the*

Worship of Nimrod and His Wife - Hislop, A. (Kessinger Publishing, 1998) p. 92

35. *Christmas* in *The Old Catholic Encyclopedia*, 1913

36. *The Mysteries of Mithra* - Cumont, F. (Dover, 1950) pp.190-1

37. *Canons of the Synod of Laodicea*, canon 29

38. *The Conversion of Constantine* - Eadie, J. W. ed. (New York, 1971) pp.13-14

39. *The Execution of Crispus* - Patrick Guthrie, in Phoenix 20, 4 (1966) pp. 325-326

40. *The Watchtower and the Ante-Nicene Church Fathers* - Partyka, M. J. (www.tektonics.org: 2005)

41. *The Annals* - Publius Cornelius Tacitus, 15:44

42. *Tractate Sanhedrin* 43a

43. *De Corona Militis* - Tertullian, chapter 3

44. Ibid., chap. 5

45. *Notes on the Wooden Doors of Santa Sabina* - Delbrueck, R. *The Art Bulletin*, Vol. 34, No. 2. (June 1952), pp. 139-145

46. *A Sense Of The Sacred: Theological Foundations Of Christian Architecture And Art* - Seasoltz, R. K. (Continuum, 2005), p. 107

47. *The Cross in Tradition, History and Art* - William Wood Seymour p. 9

48. *The Rise of Bronze Age Society: Travels, Transmissions and Transformations* - Kristiansen, K. & Larsson, T. B (Cambridge, 2005) p. 346

49. *Living Myths: How Myth Gives Meaning to Human Experience* - J.F. Bierlein (ebook)

50. Pictured in *The Codex Magliabechiano* CL. XIII.3 and discussed in *Odyssey of the Pueblo Indians: An Introduction to Pueblo Indian Petroglyphs, Pictographs, and Kiva Art Murals in the Southwest* - William M. Eaton (Turner Publishing Company, 2002) p. 85

51. *John* 10:9 & 14:6

52. *Hail Orixa! A Phenomenology of a West African Religion in the Mid-Nineteenth Century* - Peter McKenzie (New York, 1997), pp. 142 & 424

53. *Mark* 1:1

54. *Introduction to the Science of Religion* - Friedrich Muller (Montana, 2004) p. 136

55. Papyrus 105

56. Papyrus 6

57. *Codex Veronensis*

58. *Codex Corbeiensis II*

59. www.biblica.com

60. *Creeds of Christendom*, Vol. 1 - Schaff, P (ed) (1876) p. 48

61. *Description of Greece* - Pausanias (Jones, W.H.S. and Omerod, H.A. trans.) (London, 1918) 6.26.2

62. Graves p. 430

63. Frazer p. 388

64. Frazer, p. 390-391

65. *Metamorphoses* - Ovid, book 4 (Miller, I. trans.) p. 181

66. *Matthew* 4

67. *Luke* 12:49

68. *Galatians* 5:9

69. *1 Corinthians* 5

70. *Matthew* 13:33

70. *Revelation* 22:16

71. *Isaiah* 14:12

72. *The First Apology* - Justin Martyr, 66

73. Justin Martyr, 25

74. *Myth and Ritual in Christianity* - Watts, A. (New York, 1933) pp. 78-82

75. *Revista dos Orixás* - (Provenzano 2003) p. 14

76. *Looking back at the ARPANET effort, 34 years later* - David C. Walden (Massachusetts: 2003)

77. *The Trickster: A Study in American Indian Mythology* - Radin, P. (New York 1956), pp.25-28

78. Carl Jung, quoted in Radin, p. 203

79. *Bhagavad Gita*, 10.20